The great pharaoh Ramses II and his time

An exhibition
of antiquities from the Egyptian Museum, Cairo
At the Great Hall
of Ramses II,
Expo 86™
Vancouver, British Columbia, Canada

May 2–October 13, 1986

French Text   Christiane Desroches Noblecourt

Coordination   D. Avedian, R. Ben Ismaïl, H. Mikaelian

Translation   Elly Mialon

Photos   Ken S. Graetz/Graetz Inc.,
                 except in the following cases:
                 preface, objects page 35 and 45, Nefertari and 133
                 Ch. Desroches Noblecourt;
                 page 28, Fathy Ibrahim;

Printing   Ronalds Printing, Vancouver, B.C., Canada

Publishing   Canada Exim Group
                 2075 Rue University Suite 1501
                 Montreal H3A 2L1 Quebec, Canada

Legal deposit   Second quarter, 1985
                 Bibliothèque nationale du Québec

ISBN   2-9800416-0-2

Under the distinguished patronage of
His Excellency, Mr. Hosni Mubarak,
President of the Arab Republic of Egypt
and the Chief of State of Canada,
Her Excellency, Madame Jeanne Sauvé,
Governor-General of Canada

Organized by the City of Montréal
in cooperation with the Egyptian Antiquities
Organization, Cairo

under the auspices

of the Association montréalaise d'action
récréative et culturelle

Committee of Honor — Egypt

His Excellency, the Minister of Foreign Affairs and Vice Prime Minister
of the Arab Republic of Egypt,
Mr. Ahmed Esmat Abdel Meguid

His Excellency, the Minister of State for
Foreign Affairs of the Arab Republic of Egypt,
Dr. Boutros Boutros Ghali

His Excellency, the Minister of Culture of the
Arab Republic of Egypt,
Dr. Ahmed Heikal

His Excellency, the Ambassador of the Arab
Republic of Egypt to Canada,
Mr. Mahmoud Kassem

The First Under Secretary of
State of the Arab Republic of Egypt and
President of the Egyptian Antiquities Organization,
Dr. Ahmed Kadry

The former President of the
Egyptian Antiquities Organization
and member of its Board of Directors,
Prof. Dr. Gamel El Din Mokhtar

The Director General of Egyptian Museums
of the Egyptian Antiquities Organization,
Mr. Ibrahim El-Nawawy

The Director of Technical Affairs of
Egyptian Museums,
Mr. Mohamed Ahmed Mohsen

The Director General of the Egyptian Museum, Cairo,
Dr. Mohamed Saleh

To Mme Christiane Desroches Noblecourt, Commander of the Order of the Legion of Honor of France, Commandeur des Palmes Académiques, Commandeur des Arts et Lettres, Médaille d'or of the Conseil National de la Recherche scientifique, Egyptologist emeritus, author of major authoritative works on Egyptian antiquities, Chief Curator of the Department of Egyptian Antiquities at the Louvre from 1957 to 1976 and, since 1980, honorary Inspector-General of the Musées de France and Commissioner General of the Ramsès le Grand exhibition at the Grand Palais, Paris, in 1976, the Expo 86 expresses its homage, respect and gratitude.

Mme Desroches Noblecourt gave of her talent, her competence, her experience and her credibility with Egyptian authorities to assist in the presentation of the exhibition *The great pharaoh Ramses II and his time* which Expo 86 is honored and privileged to place on view.

Organizing Committee — Egypt

Mr.Ibrahim El-Nawawy
Director General of Egyptian Museums,
Egyptian Antiquities Organization

Mr.Mohamed Ahmed Mohsen
Director General of Technical Affairs
of Egyptian Museums

Mr. Essmat Ahmed
Director General of Legal Affairs

Dr. Mohamed Saleh
Director General of the Egyptian Museum,
Cairo

D. Abdel-Aziz Sadek
Assistant Director of the Centre
for Documentation on Ancient Egypt

Mrs. Saneya Abdel Aal
Assistant Director of the Egyptian Museum,
Cairo

Organizing Committee — Canada
Executives of Expo 86

Patrick Reid
Ambassador and Commissioner General
The 1986 World Exposition

Honourable Claude Richmond
Minister of Tourism/EXPO 86

Jim Pattison
Chairman and President
EXPO 86 Corporation

Walter Badun

H. Clark Bentall

Peter Brown

Harold P. Capozzi

Raymond Dagg

Don Hamilton

Lucille Johnstone

Dr. Norman Keevil Jr.

Lyall Knott

Stanley Kwok

Allan Laird

Keith Mitchell

John F. Newton

Alison Robinson

Robert Roddick

Some of the earliest forms of transportation and communications, the theme of the 1986 World Exposition, are rooted in the history of Egyptian civilizations.

Their chariots and sailing craft, which travelled a complex network of roads and canals, became models for future generations. The ancient hieroglyphic system, a form of communication based on pictorial symbols, pre-dated our own written language.

EXPO 86 is proud to welcome you to the *Ramses II and His Time* exhibition. The priceless objects that make up this extraordinary exhibition reflect the accomplishments and lifestyle of a remarkable, ancient civilization.

The great Egyptian pharaoh, Ramses II, is remembered not only as a great king, but also for his accomplishments as a builder and architect. We have constructed the Great Hall of Ramses II to house the treasures from the pharaoh's tomb, a most suitable monument for this innovative leader.

EXPO 86 visitors will have the rare opportunity to see these magnificent treasures, which date back some 4000 years. The exhibit is a tribute to the past, an historical time of great discovery, and a salute to our future.

I would like to thank Madame Christiane Desroches-Noblecourt, former Chief Curator of the Department of Egyptian Antiquities of the Louvre Museum, as well as the Egyptian Antiquities Association for their tremendous efforts in making this exhibit a reality.

Jim Pattison
Chairman, EXPO 86

Cover

Colossal statue of Ramses II — Egypt

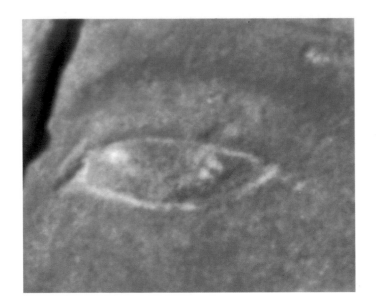

Detail

Ramses the Great

(1290-1224 BC[1])

If there is a period of Egyptian antiquity with vestiges of the past which evoke an exceptional figure of history, it is certainly that of Ramses the Great. This does not suggest that the temples, paintings and stelae, the statues and sarcophagi, the treasures and articles of daily life and all the inscriptions found on stone and papyri have enabled Egyptologists to put together all the pieces of the huge puzzle which spread from the borders of the Hittite land to the Egyptian Sudan and which are linked to the pharaoh of a country whose soil and sub-soil hold the most prestigious relics.

Indeed, eleven dynasties followed the reign of Ramses II before the Greeks and Romans occupied the "black land" (Kemet). In the interval, Egypt experienced the ordeal of invasions and dominations which scarred the entire territory. This applies to evidence of the sun-pharaoh as well as of the other kings and even more so of those who came before him in the distant past. But at the dawn of the 13th century BC, Ramses governed Egypt for 67 years, roughly from 1290 to 1224. It is therefore understandable that there are more of his monuments than of other pharaohs less covered in glory, especially those who had shorter reigns.

More than three millennia of history had slowly been covered by sand when Christian, then Moslem Egypt lost all contact with the ancient pharaonic writings. Yet from this extinct civilization rose the pyramids, obelisks—the stone needles so coveted by Rome and Byzantium—half-shattered colossi, shaken pylons and the great sphinx inexorably smothered by the desert. Imperishable names, such as those of Kheops, Khephren and Mykerinos dominated this buried world and survived the centuries. Sesostris and Ramses, in those times, were but one, though the two great kings belonged to very different dynasties—Sesostris III and Ramses II. Their signs met in the name Sesothes which confused that of one, Senwosret, with the nickname of the other, Sesu.

During his lifetime, Ramses, like all his predecessors, sought to be not only the son incarnate of the gods—the sun-god above all—but he declared himself god on earth and this deification remained throughout the ages. Travellers of classical antiquity spoke of his miraculous birth as the son of Ptah-Hephaistos (Diodorus of Sicily, I, 54 and 73).

When the priests of this god had refused Darius' wish to erect before their temple a colossus of 30 cubits comparable to those of "Sesostris the Egyptian", surrounded by his wife and children, the great king agreed that "not having been able to defeat Scythia, he had not accomplished exploits rivalling those of the Pharaoh" (Herodotus II, CX).

Everything conspired to keep the figure of Ramses II from ever fading away. Unquestionably, Ramses himself helped fashion his own lasting glory.

By carefully studying the evidence which has come down to us, a common thread may be found in the official history of each pharaoh, though it is not readily perceived. Be it from the standpoint of religion, the daring deeds of warriors, or anecdotes, Ramses left his mark on the theological concept and its commentary, on military action, the life of his era and the great problems of man.

Certainly, his reign was compatible with the long line of thirty pharaonic dynasties. Who today may claim that some initiative, attributed to him, was not a custom already respected in centuries past? Yet one may be certain that the famous drama of Amarna of the celebrated Amenophis IV Akhenaten would remain a lesson as well as an example for Ramses. How carefully did he seek the means of recovering it? What skill did he have to call upon to avoid the stumbling blocks of an excessively vulnerable idealism? What diplomacy did he impose, risking his own skin, to achieve his indisputable supremacy—that of the sun incarnate—while remaining closer to his subjects than any pharaoh before him?

He used all the means at his disposal. He was not satisfied to dominate the men of the Nile and the great chiefs of foreign nations from his far-off horizon. He spoke, he explained, he wrote, he embellished his religious and historical narratives with details taken from life and practical explanations. In short, he sought to inform, to make History. His touch, in the service of a skillful policy focusing on the needs of the moment, helped further his glory. A veritable living god, natural defender and benefactor of his people, he was the lord

[1]   K.A. Kitchen, the latest scholar to study the reign of Ramses II, proposes that 11 years be eliminated from the chronology of the New Empire starting with the reign of Tuthmosis III. This would place the period of Ramses the Great between 1279 and 1213. However, this chronology has not yet been entirely validated (cf. K.A. Kitchen, *Pharaoh Triumphant*, Warminster, 1982, p. 239).

of miracles. Anything he touched had to succeed and was thereby sublimated. In the Nubian deserts of Wadi Allaki, he sought the site of a well–that of Akita, or Akuyati, near Quban–where his father's workers had dug in vain to a depth of 120 cubits without finding water. Ramses, the young sovereign, resumed the task and, in Year 3 of his reign, made water run from under 12 cubits of sand and rock. Travelling through the desert of Heliopolis, surrounded by his mining engineers, after rallying the provinces of Canaan and eastern Palestine to the crown, in Year 8, he himself found an immense block of solid quartzite, taller than an obelisk, from which he had sculpted a colossus 20 metres high as well as other statues. Those who extracted and carved the providential stone would get their just reward.

Three years previous, he had fought the famous battle of Qadesh. There, betrayed by enemy spies, he had been pushed by his youthful recklessness into a life-threatening impasse. Courageous and keeping his wits about him, his *baraka* enabled him to face virtually singlehandedly a seemingly hopeless challenge at the start of the battle. With the hand of God assisting him in his superhuman struggle, Ramses turned fate in his favor. Twenty-nine years later, he set out to meet a princess from a faraway land who, escorted by an endless caravan, was advancing towards the country of her royal fiancé. Rain and snow slowed her passage but once Ramses became involved, the most amazing thing occurred–the sun shone, abruptly scattering the storm clouds and cold.

No one doubted his power over the elements. The time of his birth was close to a new Sothic cycle. During his first great jubilee, no one could imagine that the exceptional flood which brought Egypt an unusual harvest was mere coincidence.

His filial piety, remarkable above all others, had produced the divine promise that he would reign eternally. He sat on the throne 67 terrestrial years, tangibly demonstrating another indisputable miracle. Many of his successors, familiar with his legend, were to envy him.

*

Who exactly was this Ramses? From what context did he emerge to underscore so emphatically what others would have considered naturally granted to a son of the gods?

Ramses was not of royal lineage. This is undoubtedly a factor which must be kept in mind in attempting to understand the motives which helped shape his personality.

The 18th dynasty of the Tuthmosis and Amenophis pharaohs had died out with the last actors in the Amarnian drama. After Tutankhamun, the throne was occupied, apparently for four years, by Ay. He was succeeded by the former army chief of staff, Haremhab, who probably was married to Mutnodjmet, sister of Nefertiti. Around 1308 BC, no member of the reigning family appeared worthy of claiming the throne. Everything points to the likelihood that the 19th dynasty was, in fact, founded by one of the highest civil servants close to the old king. The officer ranked immediately after the pharaoh in terms of responsibilities. He was the vizier Pramesse, invested with the most important sacerdotal, civil and military functions, including the governor-generalship of the fortress of Tjaru, the modern El-Qantarah, Egypt's key citadel on the road to the Near East.

To date, the accuracy of this identification is based on one document, a vital document exceedingly difficult to interpret–the "Stele of the Year 400" (Cairo Museum). Its text suggests the following conclusion: initially, Ramses had to validate his ancestors' right to the throne. Certainly, like all the great kings of Egypt, he declared himself loved by the gods and presented himself as "the chosen of the Sun, dear to Amun and Ptah", master of the sanctuaries of Heliopolis, Thebes and Memphis, the three greatest cities in Egypt. In addition, he delighted in adding to this trinity–the jewel of his official theology, grouping the three forces in a single entity–the concept of the god Seth, a symbol of turbulence, even aggressivity, but also a combative power and protector of the sun. From the time of the pyramids, no one was ignorant of the divine name of Seth, incorporated in a more or less visible manner in the royal protocol. The god was so much a part of the pharaoh that the queen was "the one who sees her Horus and her Seth", that is, who lived intimately with the sovereign heir of the sun. To everyday man, Seth was the necessary evil that was dangerous to handle. The god could be invoked only with the greatest care. Thanks to mythological legend, he was sometimes considered a harmful force. Half Satan, half Prometheus, Seth unleashed storms and tempests. The animals of the desert with their red fur were devoted to him. Any Egyptian born with "flaming" hair was considered to be a follower of Seth.

To our great surprise, when the mummy of Ramses was brought to Paris to halt its disintegration due to a harmful fungus then not yet identified, several specialists of the capillary system who studied the skull before its exposure to gamma rays discovered that the roots of the pharaoh's hair were unquestionably red.

One may then legitimately wonder if this feature of Ramses II, and probably of his immediate ancestors, did not influence their attitude towards the god Seth on which "red forms" depended.

The pharaoh, in a manner of speaking, had sublimated what for others would have been a defect or, at any event, a serious disadvantage.

In the early dynasties, popular sentiment often considered Seth to be a demon and source of any evil which may have plagued Egypt. Yet naturally from the beginning of the 19th dynasty, when Seth appeared on the barque of the sun, he was considered responsible for defending the god against attacks by the serpent Apophis, the true incarnation of evil.

Ramses, son of Sethos, the first king of Egypt whose name at birth was formed with that of the god Seth, had to prove the exceptional nature of his origins and, at the same time, dedramatize, as it were, the assimilation of his father's name with that of a dreaded god. He thus had to reveal the exact identity of his divine ancestry, justify it and even glorify it. Before this time, pharaohs mounted the throne of Horus—the son of Osiris and brother of Seth, whose successors they were considered to be. Ramses himself, the chosen one of the sun, was also a descendant of Seth, "the father of his fathers". The latter were apparently originally from a western delta city, located south of the fortress of Tjaru where the locality of Hwt-Waret (Avaris) contained hovels and residences near a lake with verdant banks. Perhaps a high civil servant by the predestined name of Seth was already responsible for founding a great temple at this site to honor the god Seth.

Then Egypt was invaded and its line of fortresses, built by the pharaohs of the Middle Kingdom, were unable to protect it. Avaris fell into the hands of foreign masters the Egyptians called Hyksos. In the form of Seth, the latter undoubtedly found one of the expressions of their own god. Four hundred years later, on the fourth day of the fourth month of the Summer season (all solar symbols), the younger of the two viziers of Haremhab, Sethos, solemnly went to the ancient

site of Avaris to commemorate the pious action of his ancestors. Soon after, he was to mount the throne upon the death of his father, himself a former vizier of the pharaoh and holder of duties which had later been granted to his son. The old vizier was Pramesse, married to Lady Sitre, his queen when, upon the death of Haremhab, he became Egypt's sovereign under the name of Menpehtyre, or the first Ramses.

The "Stele of the Year 400" tells us that Pramesse was the son of a singer of Re, Lady Tia. Ramses II could well be proud of this great grandmother, through whom he would have inherited divine blood. He recalled that the distant kings of the 5th dynasty had been miraculously born into the world by the wife of a priest of Re of Heliopolis, approached by the god at the time of her nuptials.

The famous stele must have been primitively erected in the ancient city of Pi-Ramses, on the present site of Qantîr, where most of the monuments were collected for the 21st dynasty and transported to Tanis, not far away, likely because a branch of the Nile had shifted. The glorious Pi-Ramses, whose fame was celebrated by the poets of the king, already existed under Sethos I who had the façades of his houses decorated with tiles glazed in a blue shade of special luminosity so that Pi-Ramses was compared to a "turquoise city".

A third reason, perhaps, militated in favor of the stele's erection—to commemorate the building of the new capital east of the eastern delta where sovereigns were to come to live on a permanent basis. They withdrew from Thebes, which remained above all the city of Amun, god of the Empire, but which was too remote from the eastern borders of Egypt. In fact, the seat of Ramesside government was apparently still maintained at Memphis at the beginning of the reign of Ramses II.

Thus, born of an old vizier, Ramses was brought into the world by Lady Tuya (cf. 5), daughter of Raia, lieutenant-general of chariotry, and Lady Ruia. Tuya, in turn, became queen after the death of Ramses I.

The childhood of the future Ramses II was marked by exceptional circumstances. If the mathematician, Theon of Alexandria, is to be believed, the beginning of the Menophres era—probably the Greek appellation of the coronation name of Ramses I, Menpehtyre, but which, in fact, could have been applied at birth to the new dynasty, the 19th, of which Ramses I was the founder between 1313 and 1309 BC—must correspond to a phenomenon peculiar to the Egyptian calendar:

the return of the new Sothic cycle. It was, in other words, the precise moment when the two Egyptian calendars–that of the real year, which recognized the loss of a quarter day per year, and that of the fixed year, which lost a day every four years–again concurred, an event which happened only every 1,461 years. The first Sothic year of the Christian era took place around 147 BC. The blessed instant when all the seasons of the fixed civil calendar fell into place and when there could be no confusion between two systems which baffled so many scribes was naturally considered the beginning of a providential period. Ramses could not have been born at any other time– he who was the man of miracles! Through his writings and his monuments, he sought to imply a coincidence between the time of his birth and that essential date which, roughly speaking, covers the end of Haremhab's reign and the time the latter chose his two viziers to succeed him. With equal daring and insistence, Ramses showed how, "beginning with the egg", he not only was chosen by his father as heir, but was invested with the dignity of the prince-regent, in the presence of high dignitaries, before all of Egypt, in order to "participate in the state's affairs". Thus, while still almost in swaddling clothes, the young prince, the regent but not co-regent, very quickly assisted his father who endowed him, when he was about eight years old, with a generous harem. His tutor at the time may have been the future intendant of the Ramesseum treasury, Tjia, who also boasted that he taught His Majesty "from the egg" and ensured the education of the Master of the Two Lands.

This leading civil servant married Ramses' elder sister who was also called Tjia. (Their tomb has just been discovered in the Saqqara necropolis.) The "royal daughter, royal wife", Henutmire, was long considered as a second sister and wife of the king. In truth, it would appear this princess was in fact the daughter of the king or perhaps even one of his nieces. Ramses may well have had an older brother, but, in any case, the brother probably died before the death of Sethos I.

A famous text, found in Nubia, at Kuban, recounts that Ramses, at the age of ten, commanded a military unit, thus confirming his early introduction to training for the role of king. It is likely that as soon as he was strong enough and perhaps even in place of his deceased elder brother, he accompanied his father, Sethos, in an initial war against the Libyans, after campaigns launched by Sethos in Canaan and in Amurru (Palestine, Lebanon and Syria) in order to reestablish the Egyptian presence in the region. Since Amenophis III, it had been opposed and often eliminated.

*

After about 15 years on the throne, Sethos I died around 1290 BC (cf. Chronological table. Some historians place the event in 1301 BC or even 1304 BC; others, including K.A. Kitchen, according to calculations based in part on civil geneaologies, move back the date by 11 years). Ramses, as he had been called since the day of his birth, mounted the throne a full-fledged king. His confirmed coronation name was Usimaare, to which Setepenre, or "chosen by the sun", and Titenre, meaning "image of the sun", was added. The ceremony probably was held in the third month (June) of *shemu* (the last season of the year before the flood), on the 27th day.

It is generally believed the king, at the time, lived in Memphis or perhaps Heliopolis. However, certain writings he inspired could imply he already resided in the city of Pi-Ramses, not yet beautified by him.

The period of nearly three months required to prepare Sethos' mummy had passed and the river procession entered the Nile, travelling upstream to Thebes where it crossed to the left bank. Then the procession took the road to the Valley of the Kings where it would accompany the deceased pharaoh, surrounded by his funeral pomp, in his sumptuous hypogeum.

Soon after, Ramses took part in the great Festival of Opet on the right bank. All pharaohs attended this festival, especially early in their reigns. It was celebrated in honor of the pilgrimage made each year by the god Amun who travelled from Karnak to the "Opet" (divine harem?) in Luxor. It was Year 1 in the third month of the first season. The young sovereign, who must have been between 22 and 24 years old, was accompanied by his favorite wife, Nefertari. He took advantage of his stay in Thebes to select a new high priest of Amun, Nebwenenef, to replace the old pontiff who had recently died and who was the father of Paser, appointed vizier of Upper Egypt a short time previous. He laid the "first stone" of his great pylon at Luxor, decided to found his "temple of a million years"–the Ramesseum–on the left bank and vigorously urged completion of the future, gigantic hypostyle hall of Karnak, begun during his father's reign.

Like any newly crowned sovereign who travelled his kingdom to lay the foundations of his program, he went downstream to Abydos, the holy city of Osiris where the temple of his father, Sethos, had not yet been completed. The loving, respectful son gathered authorities and craftsmen and ordered prompt completion, under the best possible conditions, of the immense and famous complex which even today is greatly admired. He also demanded that the cenotaphs of the first kings of Egypt, "his ancestors", be repaired. He "laid the first stone" of his own sanctuary and decided to have two statues sculpted of the deceased king. The long dedicatory inscription of 120 lines, engraved later in keeping with his instructions under the pillar portico, still vibrates with the dialogue exchanged between father and son, one thanking the other for his solicitude, the other showing uncommon filial piety. It was in this city that Nebwenenef resided and where he was enthroned as "High Priest of Amun".

Ramses then returned to the Delta and, undoubtedly, immediately took steps to have the city of his ancestors renovated and expanded. It was a city where the temples marked the cardinal points, where homes of aristocrats nearby the palace left room for humble abodes so that the poor might also experience the joy of living. He also surely founded the great temple of Amun to the west. That of Seth, he had built in the south where the ancient districts of the city of Avaris still existed. To the east, he laid out the *temenos* of the temple of the Syrian goddess Astarte; to the north-northeast, near the great domain of Ptah, he laid out the boundaries of the sanctuary of the goddess Edjo. He also reserved an area at whose centre would rise the new palace which would "reach the horizon of the sky", not far from the great lake joining a branch of the river—"the waters of Re". A huge space was provided for infantry and chariot manoeuvres near the barracks where soldiers would be housed, grouped in major garrisons and in the region for assignment to land operations or to fighting on the pharaoh's warships. The warehouses formed a veritable district, near the famed glazed pottery workshops. Often, idyllic gardens are described. Greatly admired, they were coupled with large orchards where pomegranate and apple trees were even more numerous than date palms. Vineyards rivalling those of Memphis and the "River to the West" would supply the best wines and these would be sent to all the royal domains. There was a large indigenous and foreign population, among whom were many Semites—xenophobia was unknown in nationalist Egypt—in the city which first took the name of Pi("house") - Ramses - Beloved of Amun - Great through Victories, then, during the second part of the reign, was called Pi-Ramses - Beloved of Amon, the Great Ka of Rehorakhty.

The same year, the king seemingly returned to Upper Egypt, beyond Thebes, around Gebel-Silsileh, where the narrowing of the distance between the two banks marked a frontier for the river as it flowed into the country immediately after passing the first cataract. He paid tribute to the Nile, "the Father in which all primordial spirits are found", who ensured harvest of the *Kemet*—that is, the black earth, Egypt. He went there many times accompanied by Nefertari, and, later, by his other Great Royal Wife from the beginning of his reign, Istnofret, both mothers of a large number of his children. It was here, too, in this place essential to Egypt's life, that he proclaimed his jubilees.

No one can say with full assurance whether he travelled to the vicinity of the second cataract to select the site of the Nubian temples he founded in Abu Simbel. However, he probably ordered his viceroy of Nubia at the time, Iuny, to begin digging the sacred cave dedicated to the beautiful Nefertari. She would henceforth be transfigured, appearing as the goddess Hathor-Sothis. It is known that at the level of the Tropic of Cancer, he halted at the semi-rock temple of Beit el-Wali, which he undoubtedly had built during the latter years of his regency at his father's side. With Sethos, then beginning Year 2 of his own reign, he also sought to mark his presence on the rocky walls of the celebrated turquoise mines of Sinai.

Specific details about some periods in Ramses' life are shrouded in darkness and one is reduced to conjecture. Then, once again, there are inscriptions in a verbose style wherein praise for the child prodigy he was and complete information about his activity as king intermingle in contemporary texts from his early reign. In Nubia, once again, at Kuban (Baki), at the mouth of the gold mines of Wadi Allaki, Ramses ordered his viceroy, whose official residence, south of the Second Cataract near Amara, in the present Sudan, took the name of Pi-Ramses-mery-Amun, to see to the digging of the famous wells mentioned earlier. It was in Year 3 of the reign, in the first month of the second season on the fourth day, that the king, at Memphis itself, took the decision. That year, he likely travelled to Thebes to witness completion of the first pylon of his temple at Luxor, built before a majestic courtyard adjoining the great temple of Amenophis III. Only three years were needed to complete the task which began in Year 1 when the king inaugurated the Festival of Opet. During the same period, it is known that his astronomer-priests had assisted him in "stretching the string" to define the perimeters of his jubilee monument, today called the Ramesseum. In Year 3, he also presided over the rites of the foundation whose "astronomical hall" had certainly been completed and was perhaps even then the hypostyle whose proportions were the most harmonious of any column hall in Egypt.

These ceremonies further strengthened the divine potential of the young king who had already begun to consolidate the frontiers of his kingdom thanks "to victories by his arm". Beginning in Year 2, in fact, it would appear clear that the "warriors of the Very Green", known later by the name of Peoples of the Sea, attacked the shores of the Delta and that the king, using his vessels anchored at Pi-Ramses manned by crews of brave "marines"–the elite archers from his combined forces–captured them. They were probably the Sherden, the future Sardinians, and they were consequently integrated in his army. Two years later, they formed part of his personal guard at the Battle of Qadesh. Thanks to Ramses, "Lower Egypt could lay down to sleep (in peace)".

The king's military activity then turned almost entirely towards Asia. He undoubtedly already foresaw the day he would have to pit himself against forces united behind the king of the Hittites who was fiercely fighting him for supremacy over the Middle East. With his army, Ramses passed through his fortress at Tjaru, at the borders of Egypt, towards the end of the third year of his reign. He crossed Canaan, the country of Djahy, the future Palestine, and arrived in Phoenicia where, on his return, he had the first stele built on the shores of the Dog River (Nahr el-Kalb), north of Byblos, on the first day of the fourth month of the first season in the fourth year. He waged war against and provisionally made a vassal of Benteshina, the Amurru king. He visited his fortresses, strengthened his troops and doubtless took particular care of his elite warriors, the Nearin, whom he billeted in the back country, in Amurru, keeping them in reserve to join with the armed forces which would accompany him on his return the following year to confront his great adversary who surprised him before Qadesh, the Kinza of the Hittites, at the present Tell Nebi Mend (Laodicea), key to the country of Amurru (Amor), on the Orontes.

This contingent was to constitute the fifth division which the Egyptian army would throw into the battle and whose action proved decisive. In Year 5, during the second month of the Summer season, on the ninth day, Ramses again crossed his border. He would be surprised by the Hittite attack, the ninth day of the third month of the Summer season. The battle may have seemed uneven since the king, Muwatallis, had "united in his coalition (the strongest which had ever existed) all the barbarian nations up to the far shores of the sea . . . generously distributing money and gold from his country to lead other peoples into war with him". The alliance brought together at least 16 allied provinces, 2,500 chariots and, it would seem, two groups of warriors, one numbering 18,000 men and the other, 19,000.

Despite his genuine strategic skills and courage, the young Ramses, too impetuous, took the lead, accompanied only by his Amun division but closely followed by the Re division. He fell into a trap. Thanks to his heroism and presence of mind, he could wait for reinforcements. The outcome of the battle, if the king could consider it to be miraculous, was only a semi-defeat for the Hittites since their citadel was not occupied as it had been under Tuthmosis II and Sethos I. The Egyptians, recognizing this fact objectively, displayed on the walls a flag which was not run through with Egyptian arrows (cf. the different phases of the Battle of Qadesh at the end of the exhibition).

Obviously, space is lacking to recall all the episodes in which the clash of the armies was felt in a human context difficult to imagine today, though Ramses had the main chapters of the event illustrated in five instances on the walls of his temples. At very least, one should keep in mind that the young king went into battle accompanied by his eldest sons as well as by his royal wives whom, at the crucial moment of the battle, he ordered be "kept out of the fray". It was Prince Prehirwonmef who was commanded to take them to a zone to the west. Similar precautions must have been taken in the Hittite camp.

The extraordinary valor of Pharaoh enabled him to withstand the first shock of the enemy attack while his helpless troops dispersed. This gave the reinforcements, the Nearin, time to arrive from the west and, finally, to push back the attackers with the support of at least two of Ramses' divisions—one, that of Re, reassembled and the other, that of Ptah, arriving on the front to counter-attack from the east.

The day after the Battle of Qadesh, the king hurriedly took the route to Damascus which roughly marked the boundary between the two antagonist zones of influence in the region of Upi, south of the Amurru. Here truly began the second phase of his reign. In the two camps, the danger of the real supremacy of either power was realized. With time, a relative armistice would surely transform the situation into a durable peace but first, each side would have to affirm the extent of its power and seek to gain, if possible, some additional territorial alliances. They would also have to meet, forge and exchange draft treaties. Sixteen years were barely enough at a time when internal rivalries marked the court of the Hittite sovereign—the death of Muwatallis, who was replaced by his bastard son, Mursil II; serious disagreement between Mursil and his uncle, who finally succeeded him under the name of Hattusil.

It is a matter of record that the third Ramses in the 20th dynasty almost slavishly copied the jubilee foundation of the Ramesseum at the present site of Medinet Habu. If the outer walls of this new monument did not bear the very precise reliefs of the battles against the terrible Peoples of the Sea, and if the walls of the first courtyard showed no conclusions to the battles, historians would have had no documents from which to reconstitute events. It is therefore very likely that the walls of the Ramesseum, which have partially disappeared, carried similar scenes, dealing, naturally, with the action of the master of the kingdom during the crucial years he prepared the great peace he wanted, dreaming of chasing the Hittites from the citadel of Qadesh and of being able to deeply penetrate into Amurru country towards Aleppo and Anatolia. Only occasional vestiges in the ruins of the Ramesseum or still standing in the form of stelae built by the king himself in the conquered region remind us of his work.

He first sought to solidly win back the closest vassals. Ascalon was taken in Year 6 or Year 7 of his reign. He penetrated into Galilee. Crossing the Jordan, he passed through Jerusalem and Jericho, entering the new kingdom of Moab, beyond the Dead Sea, and engaged in a turning movement towards the south, passing by Dibon which he occupied in order to join up with the army led by his son, Amenhirkhopshef, who had taken Butartu (Raba Batora).

In Year 8, he won back Tyre, Sidon, Beirut and Byblos. Crossing the Eleutherus, he attacked the city of Dapur, in Amurru, north of Qadesh. Accompanied by at least five of his sons, he victoriously laid siege. Egyptians had not been seen there for 120 years! The assault saw the use of ladders with which his valiant princes reached the battlements of the towers. At the foot of the fortress, huge shield walls, held by solid stakes, formed something of a shell to protect the princely archers. Finally, when he passed through Nahr el-Kalb for the third time, in Year 10, he built a third stele, perhaps even upon his return from Tunip and Dapur, where his statue had been built as "Lord of the City". During secondary confrontations with the Hittites during this period, as always, he showed boldness and determination. Once again surprised by an impromptu attack, he battled for two hours without even taking the time to put on his coat of mail.

Between battles, he nonetheless did not neglect palace life, nor that of the temples. His family was continually growing, so much so that around the 40th year of his reign, according in part to figures cited at the Ramesseum and in the Nubian sanctuary of Wadi es-Sebua, he is estimated to have fathered a hundred children, born of his great royal wives, secondary queens or favorites. Many years before and at the very beginning of his time, the small temple of Abu Simbel, dedicated to Nefertari, had been completed. The first children she brought into the world are shown on the facade, against the colossi of their father. Conceivably, between Year 5 and Year 10, he ordered his new viceroy of Nubia, Heqanakht, assisted by Ashahebsed, principal cup-bearer and previously "envoy to foreign lands", his childhood friend who was probably of Syrian origin, to build his great *spéos* of Abu Simbel, on the mountain of Meha. Syrian prisoners undoubtedly were used as quarrymen. Once again, Ramses drew his inspiration from the innovations of Amenophis III and Akhenaten; at his side, he reserved a place for his mother, his wives, his sons and, increasingly, his daughters. The great southern sanctuary of Abu Simbel would be "the Book of his Reign", as it were, since he had recorded there, according to their various stages, the most marking events of his life. Naturally, he gave the Battle of Qadesh one of the largest walls of the *spéos*. On it, a vast composition appeared for the first time, contrasting with the classical presentation on "friezes" or in records. The phases of his confrontation with the Libyans and the peoples of the Middle East are also sculpted on its walls.

An easy glory is always attributed to him in regard to the rebellions he quickly put down in the countries to the south of Irem, west of the Third Cataract, in the present Sudan. The image of the king parading, as conqueror of these regions, is that of a good-natured sovereign. At the entrance and on the inside pillars of the temples, he always gave increasing importance to members of his family. His deified colossi, found in all his sanctuaries, are flanked by monumental images of his wives and smaller statues of his children. Never had the façades of rock-cut tombs or temple pylons had such an appearance. The astonishing number of his foundations in Nubia–at least five–clearly show his desire to worship the flow of the Nile, which each year during the dog-days rushed towards the parched land of Egypt. The king thus identified himself with this creative power; this is undoubtedly the reason he had himself dubbed "the husband of Egypt." All his offspring surrounding him, crowding about him, are they not the prefiguration, certainly transposed in another mode by the Romans, of those small children who jostle one another around reclining, nude, bearded spirits, allegories of the great rivers, beginning with that of the Nile, accompanied by 16 tots recalling the 16 cubits of the ideal flood?

Between the tenth and the 18th years of the reign, there are no documents dated with certainty to help determine the king's personal activity, but everything suggests he especially used this period to fight–for the first time, it would seem–in Edom, the Seir of Egyptian texts, in the country of Moab and in the Negeb. An astonishing fact should be emphasized: the small princes he battled were those who, according to the Bible, opposed the march of the Hebrews into their country. The eastern outer wall of the temple at Luxor, though partially destroyed, still bears images of these citadel attacks. A stele, found at Tell el-Hosn, the former Beth-Shan, or Beisan, sculpted in Palestinian basalt (now conserved in Philadelphia), appears to be a record of the passage of Ramses in Year 18 when he was to cross the land of Canaan to return to his country after these encounters.

It was probably during this period, sometime between Year 10 and Year 18, that the Exodus most likely took place though, in truth, no Egyptian document alludes to it. When one seeks to interpret events as they may have happened, very few details are likely to emerge. The name of Moses, certainly, is of Egyptian origin. The second and third syllables of the Egyptian name of Ramses may be recognized in it. Foreigners, Semites, Apiru (Hebrew?), withdrawn from Egyptian border regions where they had become established, may, based on customs of the time, have been educated in the royal harem of Mi-wer, in the Fayum. Other Apiru, Bedouin found throughout the Middle East, who had become sedentary in Egypt and were thereby distinguishable from the indomitable nomads, the Shosu, were then widely employed in vineyards or to manufacture bricks. In the same way–this is now known through a specific letter dating to the Ramesside period–they worked with the king's soldiers "to pull stones towards the pylon of the palace of Ramses II". Many left subordinate jobs and some even occupied high positions in court.

It does not appear possible to attribute to them rebellions or disputes which left any traces. On the other hand, at the time of Sethos, then later under Ramses II, the Timna copper mines, north of Eilat and west of Wadi Arabah in the country of Midian, one of whose priests gave his daughter in marriage to Moses, were operated by local Semite workers who labored as *free* craftsmen and sold their products to Ramses' envoys. The digs by Dr. Rothenberg have clearly proved this through the discovery, near the vestiges of a foundry, of a local temple to the goddess Hathor. Here, the golden bronze image of a serpent was even found; it was very probably a cult object. Everything suggests the Egyptians had had peaceful relations with the country of Midian. By the same token, they fought the very people who refused Moses and his people the crossing of Edom.

Should this event have had any basis in fact, what for the Egyptians would simply have been an escape, almost controlled, would, for the Apiru, have been a genuine epic.

During these years, the viziers and ambassadors of Ramses and of the Hittite king resumed their negotiations. The talks were certainly carried out at wide intervals and were even interrupted following a dynastic quarrel between the successors of the king Muwatallis. Succeeding his father, Urhi-Teshub, crowned under the name of Mursil II, behaved in such a way that his paternal uncle, who had taken part in the Battle of Qadesh as a general, finally was placed on the throne by the great men of the kingdom. Ramses was then able to conclude the long-awaited peace treaty with this major figure of Hittite history. He had just begun the 21st year of his reign.

At the time, Hattusil, the new spokesman of the king in Hittite land–he, too, was a "sun" in Hatti–presented himself as a man of great experience. The establishment of real peace between the two countries, threatened by other dangers, became an urgent imperative. The pressure of the Peoples of the Sea had to be recognized. Advanced Libyan elements–the very ones who attempted to invade the country of Hatti and who, moreover, later contributed to its downfall–infiltrated those people with barbarian names whom Ramses III was later to defeat resoundingly. Among them were the future Achaians of the classical hellenic world, Philistines, Sardinians, Dardanians, and Lycians (Luka) who fought with the Hittites in the Battle of Qadesh.

On the shores of the Tigris and Euphrates, the Babylonian dynasty was still one of splendor and power. Egypt maintained friendly relations with it, as custom required, through the marriage of one or more princesses to Ramses. The real risk came from the Assyrians who, successively breaking away from sovereigns who had dominated them, proved a grave peril for the Hittites whose frontiers they approached by invading Mitanni (Hanigalbat).

All these factors gave rise to even greater fear on the part of the Hittites than of the Egyptians. The two chancelleries agreed on a sort of treaty whose terms, carefully studied, were, once accepted, to be engraved on two silver tablets, both bearing in cuneiform the text translated in Syro-Babylonian and, deposited, one in the temple of the sun goddess in Hattushash–the Hittite capital, located in the centre of the Anatolian plateau between the Taurus and the Anti-Taurus–the other, in the temple of Re at Heliopolis in Egypt. For his part, Ramses sought to make these agreements even more important and a public event by depicting them in hieroglyphs sumptuously engraved on the walls of his temple at Karnak. Obviously, copies of the official silver originals were made and circulated in the Hittite land on clay tablets, found, in fact, in Hattushash (Boğazköy).

The miracle–yet another–is that all this evidence has been excavated by archaeologists and that more than 3,250 years later, it is still possible today, with documents at hand, to compare the precise text of the agreements and the version written for Egyptian temples. The latter was in a more verbose style but, generally speaking, closely paralleled the original. The full agreement was signed in Year 21, the first month of the second season (Winter), the 21st day of the reign of Ramses. The silver tablet intended for Egypt was brought to Pharaoh with great pomp in his city of Pi-Ramses by the six ambassadors of the two countries, including a representative of the king of Carchemish. The most important chapters of this diplomatic act begin with a reference to relations between the two countries prior to conclusion of the treaty and the initial agreements, then mention the official wording finally accepted. Next come the clauses on future relations between the two countries, a non-aggression pact, the assurance of a defensive alliance, the reciprocal desire of the sovereigns to support each other in ensuring their succession, the right of asylum and extradition, with amnesty nonetheless for all defectors.

During the final phase of negotiations, the king and the court undoubtedly left for Nubia to inaugurate the Great Temple of Abu Simbel in Year 21. This was the last time Nefertari was seen in company of the pharaoh. But, at his side, his eldest daughter, Meryetamun, is shown as a Great Royal Wife with Nefertari somewhat to the background.

The correspondence Ramses exchanged with Hattusil was certainly very extensive before and after the peace treaty. There now exist at least 26 letters from Pharaoh to the king and 13 to Pudukhepa who, like all Hittite queens, played a major role in state affairs. Certain missives dating from slightly before the event show some differences of views and, at times, engage in reproaches. However, like the previous dynasty of Amenophis II and the king of Mitanni, the monarchs had to help one another. We learn, for example, that Ramses delegated to Hattusil a physician with medicinal plants intended to cure the sterility of the Hittite's sister. In response to the request from the king of Hatti, Ramses answered impertinently and discourteously:

"As for Matanazi, my brother's sister, the king, your brother knows her. Fifty, is she? Never! She's sixty for certain! No one (in this case) can produce medicine for her to have children. But, of course, if the Sun God and the Storm God should will it . . . I will send a good magician and an able physician and they can prepare some birth drugs for her."

The transformed memory of similar events still persisted at Karnak under the Ptolemies and was translated by the priests of Khons on a stele relating the marvelous history of the healing statue of the Egyptian god, despatched to the country of Bakhtan by Ramses to save the ill princess. (The text inspired

Leconte de Lisle in one of his *Poèmes Barbares*.) Besides, the peoples of the Middle East often consulted Egyptian physicians whose reputation extended far beyond Egypt's borders. On several occasions, Ramses sent his physician, Dr. Pariamakhu, to his new allies.

Whatever the case, the Egyptian court, by sending letters to the reigning Hittite family, showed the importance it attached to the agreement which had been signed. Nefertari–Naptera, to the Hittites–sent a tablet to Pudukhepa, the great queen of Hatti, her sister, and to her royal husband. The son of Pharaoh, Sethirkhopshef, called Shoutakhapshap by the Hittites, did not fail to send, as custom dictated, a double missive to the queen and the monarch whom he called ''his father''. Tia, the dowager queen mother, also wrote to both Hattusil and to Pudukhepa, praising the happy, long-awaited event, and took the opportunity to offer the sovereign gifts of jewels and fabrics. Tia died shortly after Year 22 of the reign, probably after having seen to the ''management of business'' during the periods her son continued to pacify the territories of the Middle East.

The vizier of Upper Egypt, Paser, also wrote to the two Hittite sovereigns.

Nevertheless, despite these burning demonstrations of joy and loyalty, it would appear a period of adjustment was necessary during the few years following the agreement to establish total reciprocal confidence between the two powers. For several years, each suspected the other, as implied by letters exchanged between the two thrones. However, official friendship reigned. There was even question that Hattusil travel to Pharaoh's court for a ''summit conference''–a trip which perhaps was delayed due to the illness of the Hittite king who was afflicted with some sort of inflammation of the feet! In fact, the Hittite king continued to keep his distance, claiming to have lost none of his independence. He could not be compared to the Syrian princes who paid tribute to Pharaoh!

One must suppose that the Hittite sovereign became more conciliatory towards Ramses II when danger approached his borders. This attitude is evident at least in the terms used in a new official text reproduced on the walls of the great temples of Egypt and Nubia and which Ramses II had engraved to mark his marriage to the eldest daughter of Hattusil. It was in Year 34. Nerfertari was certainly dead and the beautiful Indo-European, who was to occupy an eminent place in Pharaoh's harem as a ''Great Royal Wife'', was anointed with oils of the engagement rites by the hands of Ramses' envoys, including a certain Huy, in the presence of Hattusil and Pudukhepa. Then she took to the road at the head of numerous and considerable presents–Ramses keenly bargained for them beforehand–''of gold, silver, copper in great quantity and slaves, horses without number, oxen, goats, sheep by the tens of thousands and productions of her country in innumerable quantity . . . They traversed remote mountains, difficult passes, O Ramses! They have now reached the borders of Your Majesty. Let the army and officials go forth to welcome them, O Ramses!'' Which is what Pharaoh did. But, wishing to avoid tiring the princess or to expose her soldiers longer than during the wars to the rigors of rain and snow which swept Syria in Winter, Ramses implored his father, the god Seth, and a new miracle occurred, that of Summer days in the Winter season. This happened, it would appear, at the boundary line between the two empires, near Damascus, at the site where the emissaries of Pharaoh were to greet the procession. The sight of the soldiers and carters of Ramses escorting the Hittite suite, headed by the governors of Upi (Damascus) and Kanakhkhi (Canaan), made a strong impression on the people of Canaan they passed in returning to Egypt: ''They ate and drank together and formed only one heart like brothers.'' It was in the third month of Winter of the Year 34 that the Hittite princess met Pharaoh in his city of Pi-Ramses. Her extreme beauty charmed him. He gave her the name of the king's wife–Maathorneferure, ''the one who sees Horus, the visible splendor of Re''. More than ever, the alliance between the two countries was to be truly effective–''Egypt and Hatti will form only one country.''

From this time forward, genuine peace seemed to reign over Egypt. While continuously conscious of the problems of the Middle East, Ramses prepared his country against possible Libyan invasion. He built a chain of fortresses from Memphis to the Mediterranean coast, west of the Delta, where Rhakotis rose on the site of the future Alexandria, then marking the coast, well beyond El Alamein, further eastward even than Marsa Matruh. The fortresses even included a temple.

The new period Ramses was entering and during which he contracted the diplomatic marriage coincided with the start of his great jubilees. The first was vividly celebrated in Year 30 of his reign by his fourth son, the high priest of Ptah in Memphis, the famous Khaemwaset, whose reputation as a scholar and magician survived the centuries. It is known he was truly the first archaeologist-prince; he carefully studied the fate of monuments from past reigns in order to ensure their restoration. A year later, a violent earthquake shook the Great Temple of Abu Simbel which had just received the royal visit during the jubilee ceremonies. Inside, Viceroy Paser, whose name was synonymous with the word vizier, saw to its repair. But the sandstone was too fragile to allow the torso of the first southern colossus of the façade to be reinstalled.

Again, with the help of the vizier Khay, Khaemwaset also conducted his father's jubilee ceremonies which he "announced throughout the earth" for the years 34, 36 or 37 and 40. From the Year 35, Merenptah, the king's 13th son, organized the jubilees. Thus, Ramses experienced 13 commemorations. The longer the reign lasted, the more the sovereign saw wives and heirs vanish from around him. The first of those who had replaced Nefertari and Istnofret in the role of Great Royal Wife, besides numerous secondary wives and innumerable concubines living in his harem, was Bintanath, daughter of Istnofret and Ramses. She must have married her father before Year 34, even giving the king a daughter, shown on the walls of her tomb in the Valley of the Queens. Before his union with Maathorneferure, Ramses had already married at least two of his daughters–Meryetamun, daughter of Nefertari, and certainly also Nebttawy. Ramses also mourned the death of many of his sons. The list of princes shown on his official monuments includes only offspring of the Great Royal Wives. At Wadi es-Sebua, in Nubia, at least 30 are mentioned. For the most part, they seem to be given in chronological order and their names also include variants, such as Montuhirkhopshef who, on occasion, is called Sethirkhopshef, or the eldest of all, Amenhirkhopshef, once named in the temple of Beit el-Wali as Amenhirwonmef. The latter, as well as Rehirwonmef, were both sons of Nefertari. On the other hand, Ramses, the second son, and Khaemwaset were sons of Istnofret. Then came, in order, the fifth to the 13th sons: Montuhirkhopshet, Nebenkharu, Meryamun, Amenemwia, Sethi, Setepenre, Meryre (the 18th son of Ramses was also called Meryre), Horhirwonmef, and, finally, Merenptah where we stop. In fact, this 13th son was Ramses' successor. All his elder brothers passed away during the long reign of their father, much like the heirs of Louis XIV later on.

Over the years, Pharaoh had affirmed his peerless divine nature. The year following his marriage with the foreign princess, in Year 35, he had built in the courthall of his temple at Abu Simbel a large rectangular stele covered with a famous inscription known as the "Decree of Ptah". In it is found confirmation of his union with the daughter of the great king of Hatti. Henceforth, Ramses declared himself the son of Ptah, god of Memphis, master of his jubilees and his divine father. At the back of the sanctuary which the sun penetrated almost completely twice a year–now on October 20 and February 20–the king, through his statue, received the emanations of the sun, in the same way as Re and Amun who flank him and with whom he is one. However, on the walls of the same temple when it was founded, the king was satisfied to be portrayed bearing offerings, especially to the divine couples of Heliopolis and Thebes. Later, he ordered his sculptors to amend the decorations by introducing his own image into the god couple. These changes are still readily visible on the walls of the great *spéos*.

He pursued his experience in the country of Nubia, chosen, it seems, because it was closer to the arrival of the nutritive flood. He therefore built the temple of Derr, dedicated to the king and to Reherakhty. But when the *spéos* of Gerf Hussein was dug, where Ramses and Ptah merged in a single person, and that of Wadi es-Sebua for Amun and Ramses together, total symbiosis had occurred–the god-king was directly represented, without alterations, in the bosom of the divine family on the reliefs which cover the walls. Pharaoh pays tribute to his own image.

The construction of the latter temple mentioned the Tjemehu whom Merenptah had to fight. A stele found nearby the temple and dedicated by the officer Ramose reveals that in Year 34, His Majesty (Ramses II) had decreed that his viceroy in Nubia, Setau, and men of the regiment called "may-Amun-protect-his-son" be ordered to capture the people of the country of Tjemehu to work on construction in the temple of Ramses, beloved-of-Amun-in the-house-of-Amun", or Wadi es-Sebua. He undoubtedly was referring to the Libyans of Marmarique, who were light-skinned, or to a related ethnic group who lived in the oases of Kurkur and Dunkul. But the danger did not yet threaten the king directly.

The latter part of Ramses' reign certainly passed without major incident, at least in terms of the history of the country. Perhaps new monuments will one day be uncovered which will shed special light on the old age of the great king. It is known that a second Hittite princess, the sister of the first, had, due to her age, entered the harem of the sovereign near the present Medinet Gurob, that of Mi-wer, whose workshops continued to weave the finest linens for these princesses.

Bowed with age, having mourned beloved wives, including the dearest of them all, Nefertari, having seen his first 12 sons die, Ramses seemed to perpetuate himself over endless years, in keeping with the wishes of his father. The lustre of his reign, his glittering actions which bordered on the supernatural, the great peace he had established with the other "sun" of the country of the Hittites, the majesty and quantity of his religious foundations bore testimony over many years to the divine quality of his ancestors and the indisputable influence of his person. At Thebes especially, he took great pains not to associate himself officially with kings whose memory could one day be called into question. It thus becomes evident how careful he was not to provoke the clergy of Amun. Similarly, in the long procession of statues of ancestors of the crown, sculpted into the wall of the Ramesseum, on the occasion of the festivals of Min, he took exceeding steps to show neither the image of Queen Hatshepsut or that of the actors in the Amarnian drama, nor Amenophis IV, Smenkhkare, Ay or Tutankhamun. The line of sovereigns after Amenophis II resumed with Haremhab, the master of his close forebears. Yet Ramses was less entitled to the throne than Hatshepsut. And had he not drawn from Amarnian theses the very basis of his own myth? He would have wanted to approach his civil servants, soldiers and humble subjects directly. He prided himself on informing them personally.

He had opened certain sanctuaries to the hope of man and, whatever the case may be, he had labored to establish peace by broadening dialogue with the adversary as no one before him had ever attempted.

During the 67th year of his reign–that is, around his own 88th or 90th year–as the hallowed words put it, "the falcon took flight, the divine flesh went to join the force from which it had emerged". Merenptah, the son of Istnofret, was crowned while the mummy was being prepared. Once again, an impressive funeral procession sailed the Nile to the rock-cut tomb–built at the entrance to the Valley of the Kings, on the western side of the mountain–whose construction by the craftsmen of the Theban necropolis had been overseen many times by his great vizier of the south, Paser.

Of the ritual treasure, certainly a fabulous one, nothing remains since the tomb, like those of the sovereigns surrounding it, was looted at the end of the 20th dynasty. When inspectors of the necropolis noted the tomb had been violated, the alleged thieves were put on trial. It began, with regard to the burial places of Ramses II and of his father, Sethos I, in Year I of the reign of Ramses IX, the fourth month of the last season of the year, on the 15th day. It is known that a group of royal mummies protected by priests from complete destruction but deprived of their sumptuous equipment was sheltered in the tomb of Sethos I. But when it became apparent that the burial vault no longer offered every guarantee of safety, the priests took advantage of the funeral of the first prophet of Amun, Pinudjem II, during the 21st dynasty, buried in the tomb of Queen Inhapy in an amphitheatre in the mountain near Deir el-Bahri, to continue to transform this burial site into a hiding-place. The latter served as a repository for most of the pharaohs' mummies, saved from looting and placed near that of Amenophis I who had already been reburied there.

Thus, surrounded by his peers, Ramses II rested on the western flank of the Theban mountain, separated from the fertile plain by the hill of Gourna. The secret location was discovered by peasants who, from 1871 to 1878, sold the papyri and objects found there for their personal profit. The authorities, alerted only in 1878, reacted energetically and rapidly. They entered the burial vault July 6. The transfer of the royal bodies from the hiding-place to the boat waiting on the river was carried out in exactly eight days. When it raised anchor for Cairo, peasants on both banks of the Nile gathered to hail the venerable remains with cries of mourning and prayers which would have done honor to the ancient official mourners. Among the remains was the mummy of Ramses, Egypt's Light Pharaoh.

Ch. Desroches Noblecourt

Chronology

3100   Beginning of history
Unification of Egypt
Appearance of writing

3100 - 2700   **Thinite period:** 1st and 2nd dynasties

2700 - 2200   **Old Kingdom:** 3rd to 6th dynasties
Pyramid age (Kheops, Khephren, Mykerinos)

2200 - 2060   **1st intermediate period:** 7th to 11th dynasties
Troubled period

2060 - 1785   **Middle Kingdom:** 11th and 12th dynasties
Reigns of Montuhotep, Amenemhat, Sesostris

1785 - 1554   **2nd intermediate period:** 13th to 17th dynasties
Disorders
Foreign invasion by the Hyksos

1554 - 1080   **New Kingdom:** 18th to 20th dynasties
1554 - 1305: 18th dynasty
Reigns of Tuthmosis and Amenophis
Religious reforms by Amenophis IV - Akhenaten
Tutankhamun restores the cult of Amun
1305 - 1196: 19th dynasty

Ramses I	1305 - 1303
Sethos I	1303 - 1290
Ramses II	1290 - 1224[1]
Merenptah	1224 - 1214
Amenmesses	1214 - 1210
Sethos II	1210 - 1204
Siptah and Tewosret	1204 - 1196

1196 - 1080: 20th dynasty
Setnakht, Ramses III and the last Ramessides

[1] Cf. note, first page of the introduction.

1080 - 332   **Late period:** 21st to 30th dynasties
1080 - 946: 21st dynasty
Joint reigns of the kings of Tanis and "divine worshippers of Amun" (and the high priests of Thebes)

Psusennes I 1054 - 1004, etc.
Siamun   979 - 960

946 - 332:   Period of foreign invasions–Libyan, Ethiopian and Persian. Saite revival in the 26th dynasty: 664 - 525

332:    Conquest of Egypt by Alexander the Great
Reign of the Ptolemies until the Roman conquest

The builder-king

In history, Ramses the Great preserves the reputation, more than any other pharaoh, of having covered Egypt with innumerable monuments. The most important cities and all the holy places bear his mark. Certainly, he could not innovate everywhere. Very often, he pursued the work of his predecessors–at Karnak, Abydos, Gourna, Memphis, Heliopolis, Fayum, Hermopolis, in Nubia and even in Asia.

Any political or religious activity, as a logical conclusion, led to edification of a temple, the erection of a stele or an obelisk, the construction of a fortress, the foundation of a city (the empire was dotted with cities bearing the name of Ramses). Sometimes, the king was satisfied to leave the mark of his passage in the sanctuary he had visited, maintained and perpetuated, as shown by the column fragments exhibited in this room. The king should not be labelled a usurper. He respected the names of his predecessors (here, for example, the protocol of Tuthmosis IV has remained intact). Was he not the incarnation of divine authority expressed by the royalty of which each pharaoh was a link in an indestructible chain?

Often, only parts of foundations of ruined temples remain as witnesses to long-lived rites in which the gods presided over the work of architects and quarrymen. But always, be it through the orientation of a new sanctuary, the recognition of a newly discovered quarry or the choice of a gigantic block of stone from which colossi of Pharaoh would be extracted, Ramses is present, both as the Great Magician of miracles he proposed and the Father of the Egypt he would know how to care for.

From the depths of the quarries–all under royal authority–came the material from which were sculpted the precious portraits and imposing forms of pharaonic power. What then may be said of these mountains from whose bodies the sanctuaries had been shaped? In Nubia particularly, more than six spéos, or hemispéos, were built, at the back of which, according to a route marked with images of royal renewal, Pharaoh appeared on the divine bench, among the great gods of the Empire, merged with them and expressed them all–Amun, the hidden power, Ptah, the world renewed, Rehorakhty, the sun which endows all things with life, and he, Pharaoh, Ramses, which the sun brought into the world, born of the radiance whose often aggressive, bellicose, dynamic ardor Seth, patron of his gens, evokes and without which nothing could be brought to a successful conclusion.

These four divine concepts were patrons of the four army divisions of Pharaoh which we follow into the Battle of Qadesh. Some temples do not have the classic seated statues of the king before their pylons. At Karnak-North, or at Armant, for example, and sometimes in Nubia, as at Wadi es-Sebua, is found the very characteristic image of His Majesty bearing signs–a small curly wig surrounding the colossal face, holding against each of his arms a staff crowned with a divine symbol (cf. the colossus of the king, 1). The significance of the sanctuary is strengthened and much research is still needed to fully grasp its meaning.

Pharaoh's architects were uncommon personalities. Contributing to the edification of divine houses, these scholar-technicians escaped the anonymity of the multitude of sculptors, "contour scribes", authors of reliefs and art craftsmen who decorated the monuments and created treasures and religious furniture. Often the beneficiaries of the 110 years of life with which scholars were gratified, they were worshipped as in the case of Imhotep in the 3rd dynasty and Amenophis-son-of-Hapu, in the 18th dynasty. One of the architects closest to Ramses, May, son of a chief of works at Thebes, is part of this line, but is reduced to modest proportions by the omniscience of his king. His glory seems more discreet than that of his predecessors. However, he built the most prestigious complexes at Memphis and Heliopolis–one of Ramses' favorite cities–where among the constructions emerging from the shadow of the obelisks is an immense hypostyle hall rivalling in splendor with that of Thebes. In addition, May created monuments which made Pi-Ramses-Great-of-Victories the most dazzling beacon-city of Egypt.

Colossus of Ramses II as a votary of Montu and Rat-tawy

Catalogue entry number in the Cairo Museum: 44,668

Dimensions
Total height: 2.44 m
Max. width (shoulders): 1 m
Width (base): 0.73 m
Depth: 1.03 m

Medium
Pink granite

Technique
Lower members deliberately heavy
    Face intentionally broadened

Condition
Very good

Provenance
Temple of Armant

Date
Ramses II

Bibliography
Drioton, *Les quatre Montou de Médamoud, palladium de Thèbes* in
    CdE 12, July 1931, pp. 259-270.
Mond and Myers, *Temples of Armant*, London, 1940, pp. 4, 15, 49

Desroches Noblecourt *et alii*
Catalogue of the Ramses le Grand exhibition, Paris, 1976, No. XII, pp.
    64-67

This magnificient statue of pink granite, bearing all the marks of the colossal, was built by Ramses before the temple of the god Montu whose vestiges still remain on the left bank of Thebes at Armant, called Hermonthis by the Greeks and which, in Antiquity, was known as the Heliopolis of the South (Iwnu-Shemau).

The god Montu, who was so preponderant in the Theban capital during the 11th dynasty that he figured in the names of kings, surpassed the supremacy of the god Amun and affirmed himself as the no less powerful protector of the crown and weapons, and not of war as has been claimed. His four sanctuaries at the four geographic corners of the temple of Amun–Karnak-North, Medamud, Tôd and Armant–formed the palladium of the divine city–its magical protection. He is often shown with the head of a falcon. His sacred animal was the bull, Buchis. His female counterpart, the ancient goddess Tjenenet, often appears as an aspect of Rat-tawy, that is, the "Feminine-Sun-of-the-Two-Lands". Worshipping them, the king is in the attitude of dynamic force, the left foot forward, wearing his two "signs", one crowned with the disked head of the falcon, complemented by a necklace on his chest, and the other with a woman's head adorned with the same wide necklace (*wesekh*). His wig bears the horns of the goddess Hathor which contain the image of the sun, also decorated with a serpent, the *uraeus*. On the two staffs, the inscription columns recall that the king made a commemorative monument to his father Montu, Lord of Heliopolis (of the South), as well as to his mother, Rat-tawy. But he adds that for him as well as for her, he undertook the act of making a living statue of Re. Thus, the statue of the king here dedicated incarnates the living image of the sun, rendered by that of the king.

It is undoubtedly in this context that the face, so broad, of the colossus must be interpreted. A solar globe, it is surrounded with a wig and girded with a *seshed* headband, dominated by the *uraeus*, whose fine curls evoke a constant quivering of life, complemented by the long artificial royal beard. Also to be noted under the wig, above the eyebrows, is a decorated headband in the centre of the image of the solar disk. This concept also explains the massiveness of the body which, despite its remarkable form, evokes the heaviness of the ankles and legs, the thickness of the feet, the force of the pink granite exposed to the heavenly body which gives life to all things.

The base of the two staffs rests on the rectangular stone recalling the earth. The stone, bearing the names of Ramses, Lord of the Jubilees, was placed on a wide base with a groove set in the front. It is still on view at the Cairo Museum whose collection, like the statue, it joined in 1913.

The undeniable power emanating from this colossal composition is further complemented by a monumental crown whose fastening hole, 0.12 m in diameter, is still visible at the top of the wig. On each shoulder, the colossus is marked very deeply with a mysterious sign which perhaps suggests three rays of the sun. At the rear, what is called the dorsal pillar occupies the entire height of the statue. The inscriptions refer to the royal protocol, placed under the protection of the two divinities whose emblems he bears. The dual mention of the Sed festival evokes the numerous jubilees of the king.

The naked torso is adorned only at the base of the neck with a double-strand necklace, made of a series of gold, lens-shaped rings. Bracelets are discreetly incised. His only apparel is an archaic loincloth, made fashionable again by its form, rising at the back above the waist and by the pleated linen of which it is fashioned. In the front, under the prophylactic cheetah head, is a flap which falls to the knees. It is the jeweled apron which was apparently rigid and ended at the base in seven disked *uraei*. The buckle of the belt, whose form follows the movement of the loincloth around the abdomen, bears the coronation name of the king, Usimaare-setepenre, Powerful like Montu.

Of all the temples still standing on the shores of the Nile, the complex of sanctuaries of Abu Simbel is the only group of religious structures where a small sun sanctuary has been preserved with the majority of elements which allowed its operation.

Certainly, Egyptologists have been able to establish that as early as the 5th dynasty, the notion of sun altars existed. They recall, thanks to forms expressed in stone, the essential significance of the rites. Thus, on the site of Abu Gurob, south of Giza, a large base supported a huge stone obelisk. Egyptologists agree it materialized the creative role of the sun in the genetic heat which spreads throughout the world. Before the divine petrified member was built a device on which offerings were to be laid. The latter was square in form, like the very base of the obelisk, with each of its sides directed towards the four corners of the world. The concept has been preserved to the present day through the notion of the four cardinal points. But the altar was also adorned with symbolic signs which served to reinforce its message. Its sides consisted of four giant hieroglyphs with a table of offerings seen in profile, dominated by the silhouette of the bread of the essential offering. In the centre was a circle which, unequivocally, could only express the image of the sun.

Unfortunately, it is impossible to reconstruct the operation of the rites which must have taken place before evocations of the most powerful of cosmic phenomena, but one may be certain that beginning in these long-ago periods, scholar-priests, through the ritual, sought to maintain the apparently harmonious progression of the star during the 24 hours of the day and night, and also during the 365 days of the calendar which had three typical seasons of four months, recalled in reliefs on the temple's walls.

In the following periods, similar devices must certainly have been integrated in the religious foundations to enable priests to maintain the essential dialogue with this luminous source of light. But nothing survives of the monuments which dissappeared or were merged with later constructions or, often built of beautiful blocks of limestone, were destroyed by lime-burners of the Coptic period. It is not until the New Kingdom that one may find new traces of sun altars in the remaining temples. They certainly evolved but the vestiges which remain do not make it possible to reconstruct, in a precise manner, the accessories complementing them. The three most famous may be cited–the one whose bases remain intact north of the Hatshepsut complex at Deir el-Bahri, that which still dominates the northern part of the famous Akh-Menu of Karnak and, finally, that in the temple of Sethos I at Gourna, also located in the Septentrion.

During the reign of Amenophis IV-Akhenaten, the great zealot of the sun globe, one would expect to find an impressive array of evidence making it possible to evoke the full development of the rites whose universality had been advocated by Akhenaten. However, the reform he undertook was founded essentially on the simplification of a ritual; he denounced useless deviations. One can see on the walls of Amarnian tombs the very simple attitudes of devotion of the sovereigns, whose gestures are oriented solely towards the image of the star, complemented by rays with hands directed towards its creatures. The representations of the great altar fail to satisfy our curiosity, so much have they been plundered.

The ruins of the reformer's capital particularly show that it was square in form and that several steps led to it. However, one may assume that the cult of the diurnal hours at least had to concur with the progression of days and seasons of the year, as proved by the presence of the 365 offering tables in the great temple of the city of the globe of Aten.

The discovery of the vestiges of the sun complex at Abu Simbel, made in 1909 when the great temple was cleared by Barsanti, architect of the Egyptian Antiquities Department, was an event for Egyptology since it involved the most complete grouping of this type ever found. Located north of the great temple and hidden by the sands and rubbish, the small edifice, open to the sky, was still in place, though partially collapsed. The elements patiently put back in place made it possible to evoke the liturgy of the Ramses II period which ensured the continuity of rites already more than 2,000 years old. A rectangular courtyard had been sculpted at the base of the septentrional knoll of the great temple measuring 3.50 by 4.70 m. Its façade consisted of a wall of small sandstone blocks, dominated by two temple pylon towers, separated by a huge opening. The northern, western and southern walls were built into the rock. The latter part of the edifice was pierced by an entrance way, with access by four steps linking the terrace of the great temple with the sun courtyard. Inside, the walls were adorned with reliefs among which, from west to north, could be distinguished the barque of the diurnal star disappearing over the horizon, with jackals barking at it. On the prow, the image of the returning sun at the end of its nocturnal course was illustrated by a child kneeling on a background of lotuses. In contrast, on the northern wall, the barque conveyed the diurnal symbol of the star–a man with a falcon's head.

If the interior of the walls of the sanctuary allude to the various aspects which the sun took during the 24 hours of its apparent march, on the outside wall, which is at the base of the two pylon towers, the ornaments evoke the two classic aspects of the divine in all the temples of Nubia–to the south is the reminder of Amun, to the north, that of Rehorakhty, both oriented as they are found in statues at the back of the temple.

The exceptional interest of the excavated ruins resided in the elements of furniture which complemented them. The altar, built of solid sandstone, square in form and dominated by the Egyptian groove, supported four images of standing baboons with thick coats, the front legs raised in the attitude of adoration. The decoration of the tombs and funerary papyri of the New Empire frequently represent the evocation of the sunrise, complemented by the image of these little green baboons, products of the primeval spirits of Hermopolis, whose action was said to have made the star emerge from the darkness. Situated at the four corners of the tray, the baboons, in fact, must have occupied the place of future angle ornaments, one of the first of which is that facing the tomb of Petosiris at Tuna el-Gebel. The baboons thus venerated the image of the sun whose first rays, adored by the priest perched at the top of the four steps leading to the altar tray, rose from the eastern mountain and passed through the two towers of the small pylon, then, flanked by the two obelisks, responded to the call of the four baboons. Against the northern wall of the courtyard, on a grooved Egyptian base built into the rock, a small nook without ceiling and with a huge opening looking southwards, like the entranceway, had been built to contain two sandstone idols. One represents the heavy baboon of the god Thoth, seated with its paws on his knees. The head is crowned with the image of the crescent of the moon. The other is an enormous scarab whose *clipeus* is dominated by the image of the sun adorned with a serpent. The identity of these divine forms is obviously recognized, but the outside walls of the sanctuary complement this information since, on the baboon's side, the bas-relief of Ramses II may be contemplated, wearing a *khepresh*, offering vases of wine to the god Thoth, in his ibis form, while on the other side, Pharaoh wearing the *af-net*, offers the same vessels to the god Rehorakhty.

It should be noted that in this small sanctuary, the evocations of the moon–the baboon of Thoth–and of the sun–the scarab showing Rehorakhty–have been placed where they belong if they are to be considered elements in their nocturnal stations. The moon rises in the east and the sun sets in the west, in the form of Atum, to "recharge its battery", in order to reappear as a scarab.

The sun altar of Abu Simbel must therefore have had the role not only of making the diurnal star rise at the end of the day, but also of leading it to its setting west of the mountain. In the east, the moon (Thoth) took over to dispense the nocturnal light. Religious texts often called this the right and left eye of the god, the latter, in fact, receiving the light of the former, as the Egyptians had observed. This succession of days and nights made up the cycle of the solar year of 365 days (1/4), opened by the arrival of the flood whose spirit is shown on the inside of the eastern wall.

Once again, through concrete and often animal images, the Egyptian scholar-priests knew how to express the grand laws of Nature and we are again indebted to Ramses II for having built such a complex north of his great temple.

All the accessories of this divine "machinery" were transported, on the orders of Maspero, to the Cairo Museum and the exhibition Ramsès le Grand in Paris was an opportunity for many Westerners to admire this strange composition in the Grand Palais. It is quite obvious that these sandstone sculptures are too vulnerable to remain exposed out-of-doors on the site itself, but it is to be hoped that faithful replicas will now be made to enable the numerous visitors to the great Nubian temple to profitably contemplate the sun altar, complemented by elements which make it such an exceptional complex.

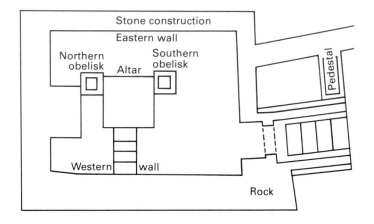

Sun altar

Catalogue entry number in the Cairo Museum: 42,955

Dimensions
Base (still in place at Abu Simbel)
Height: 1.45 m
Length: 1.25 m
Width: 1.25 m

Baboons
Height: from 0.92 m to 0.991 m
Width of the base: from 0.26 m to 0.286 m
Depth of the base: from 0.37 m to 0.435 m

Medium
Stuccoed Nubian sandstone, painted white, red and yellow

Technique
Intaglio engraved reliefs and hieroglyphs (on the original base
    still on site)

Condition
The colors have been substantially altered. One obelisk and one
    sanctuary were heavily damaged and have been restored.

Provenance
Abu Simbel, centre of the sun sanctuary

Date
Ramses II

Bibliography
Barsanti, *Les temples immergés de la Nubie*, report, I (1911), pp.
    150-151
Masporo, *La Chapelle nouvelle d'Ipsamboul, ZAS.* XLVIII (1911), p. 94

Desroches Noblecourt *et alii*
Catalogue of Ramsès le Grand exhibition, Paris, 1976,
    No. XXXIV, p. 153

On a square base with a slightly narrowed top, cut into the sandstone rock, was sculpted a cornice of typically Egyptian form—a reminder of the palm branch frieze which dominated the buildings of ancient Egypt. It seems virtually certain that the small baboons standing on their hind legs in an attitude of adoration must have been located at the four corners, not facing the exterior, as one might have thought, but inward so they might greet the incandescent ball of the sun they made emerge. It is obvious that these hamadryads evoke the four male spirits of Hermopolis who, according to mythology, were the sires of the sun. The square altar on which they stood was naturally marked with the names of Ramses, beloved of Atum and Amun.

Small *naos*

Catalogue entry number in the Cairo Museum: 42,955
Cairo general catalogue: 70,005

Dimensions
Height: 1.095 m
Width: 1.15 m
Max. depth: 0.93 m

Medium
Nubian sandstone; text and figures painted in yellow

Technique
Intaglio engraved relief. Engraved hieroglyphs.

Condition
Colors have been altered.

Provenance
Abu Simbel, northern side of the sun sanctuary

Date
Ramses II

Bibliography
See baboon altar
Roeder, *Naos*, Catalogue général . . . du Musée du Caire (Cairo, 1914),
      No. 70005, pp. 22-24, pl. 6

Desroches Noblecourt *et alii*
Catalogue of Ramsès le Grand exhibition, Paris, 1976,
      No. XXXIV, pp. 156-157

A small, trapezoidal-shaped building without a back or a ceiling was placed against the northern wall of the enclosure. It had a cornice, eastern and western side walls and a southern façade with a huge opening which never seems to have been closed by shutters. The building, composed of sandstone slabs, rested on a base with the names of Ramses topped by the image of the sky or of the sun disk. The absence of a roof makes it possible to identify it, from the outset, as a tabernacle devoted to luminous entities which could penetrate it from everywhere. On the right hand of the opening is the birth name of the king and, on the left, his coronation name. The eastern and western walls are each adorned with an offering scene. In the east, the king, standing on the ground and wearing sandals, offers vases of wine to the ibis-headed god Thoth. The sovereign wears his crown, the *khepresh*. On the other side, Ramses, dressed in identical ceremonial loin-cloth, pays tribute in the same attitude. He wears a sort of head-cloth and officiates before the disked god Horus-of-the-Horizon. The only difference between the scenes is the presence of two stools before Horakhty while, before Thoth, there is only one. The accessories, however, are the same.

Astral statues

Catalogue entry number in the Cairo Museum: 42,955

Dimensions
Baboon
Height: 0.92 m
Width of the base: 0.33 m

Scarab
Height: 0.69 m
Width at paw level: 0.43 m

Medium
Stuccoed Nubian sandstone, painted in white, yellow and red

Technique
The baboon is poorly sculpted.

Condition
Good

Provenance
Abu Simbel, sun sanctuary, *naos*

Date
Ramses II

Bibliography
See small sanctuary

Desroches Noblecourt *et alii*
Catalogue of Ramsès le Grand exhibition, Paris, 1976,
No. XXXIV, pp. 158-160

Inside the small tabernacle open to the temple, heavy stone statues were placed, literally side by side, with no space between them. As has been suggested, they are the nocturnal aspects of the sun and the moon which takes over in the form of the baboon of Thoth. On the other side and on a very thick base, a huge scarab announces the sun replenishing its strength.

The hamadryad baboon with such a characteristically heavy green coat seems to have been covered here with dabs of red paint, as is the case with the four baboons of the sun altar. A male, it squats in the very attitude of the animal form of the god Thoth, with the paws on the knees of its hind legs. To clearly underline the fact that it is one stage in the awakening of the sleeping star, it wears on its chest a "pectoral" pendant with the image of the winged scarab. On its head is the flattened disk of the moon, supported by the image of the ash-grey crescent.

The anatomical details of the heavy scarab seem more carefully shaped than those of the ape. The scarab has a highly prominent *clipeus*, as if the beetle were emerging from the bowels of the earth. One is fascinated by its eyes in relief. Attention is also drawn to its almost aggressive front legs. Its thorax is dominated by a huge disk adorned with a straight *uraeus*. It recalls another scarab of even more beautiful workmanship, produced under Amenophis III, sculpted in pink granite and located north of the sacred lake of Karnak.

Like the rising sun, it seems to emerge to take its morning bath in the primeval waters.

3

Column drums with the name of Tuthmosis IV, reused by Ramses II

Catalogue entry number in the Cairo Museum: 41,560

Dimensions
Max. height: 1.62 m
Diameter: 0.96 m (approx.)

Medium
Painted sandstone with a white background. The background of the
    hieroglyphs of Tuthmosis IV are yellow; the decoration of
    Ramses II is blue, blue-green, red and yellow.

Technique
Intaglio engraved texts and decoration

Condition
Three bases preserved

Provenance
Elephantine Island

Date
Tuthmosis IV and Ramses II

Bibliography
Porter-Moss V, p. 226
Morgan, Bouriant, Legrain, Jéquier, Barsanti, *Catalogue des
    monuments et inscriptions de l'Égypte antique*, 1st series,
    Tome I, p. 113

Desroches Noblecourt *et alii*
Catalogue of the Ramsès le Grand exhibition, Paris, 1976,
    No. X, p. 57

The three column drums were found on Elephantine Island, among the foundations of a monument built by order of Trajan (end of the first century AD). In fact, they come from a building which had been built by order of Tuthmosis IV. At the time, fluted columns were much in fashion. They were found in Egypt from the beginning of the Old Kingdom, then in the New Kingdom as the prototype of the doric column. As sole decoration, they bore a vertical line of hieroglyphs pertaining to the protocol and names of the builder king. Under Ramses, the approach changed. Gradually, though the fluted column tended to disappear, the shaft of the papyri-shaped column was covered with reliefs united by scenes. The most beautiful examples may be admired in the hypostyle hall of the Ramesseum, the jubilee temple of Ramses II.

Here, we see a construction which was not "usurped" by Ramses, as he has often been accused of doing—he respected the names of his predecessor—but which received the mark of the reigning sovereign to recall his presence in the venerable temple, naturally still in use during his reign.

Despite the vicissitudes these stones suffered, the colors have been partially preserved. It is even now a feast for the eyes to find on the feathers of the falcon which dominates the pharaoh and on the figure of the king himself yellow, red and turquoise blue colors which still illuminate the relief, giving some idea of the pure tones on white background which enlivened all these surfaces under the rays of the sun and which made the scenes lining the walls inside the temples phosphorescent.

The claws of the falcon hold the *shenu* ring, a sort of seal evoking the sun's circuit and which, allongated, would become the cartouche surrounding the royal names. Thus protected by the divine seal, Ramses, wearing the famous *khepresh* headdress—the body of the protective serpent on it is coiled on his forehead—was probably turned towards the divinity. Above all, it will be noted that the plant offering he holds in his hands could also be addressed to his ancestor, Tuthmosis IV, recalled here in a column of text. Under the forward wing of the bird are shown the two last names of the royal protocol—first, the coronation name at left, Usimaare-Setepenre, dominated by the title "(king) of the South and (king) of the North", followed by the epithet "son of the Sun" which gives the birth name, "Ramess(u)-meryamun, endowed with life like the sun".

The two large flaps suspended from the headdress of the king at neck height and made of fine pleated linen fall to his waist. Though many details have disappeared, one may still distinguish the vestiges of the great transparent robe with wide sleeves in front of his right arm. Under this piece of apparel appears the loincloth held by a wide belt which narrows in front and closes over the navel, visible at the height of the belt with the coronation name of Ramess(u)-Usimaare on it. His chest is adorned with the wide necklace (*wesekh*) on which, at the base of the neck, was placed a double coil very probably made of gold elements. He lifts to the height of his face a bouquet of three lotus flowers whose supple stems form a loop held in his fingers. The offering thus presented is accompanied by a heavy "mounted" bouquet of several tiers which he holds in his right hand like a cane. The bouquet suggests the idea of a festival, of rebirth, New Year's Day, and, consequently, of victory.

Unnumbered

Statue of Vizier Khay

Catalogue entry number of the Cairo Museum: 37,406

Dimensions
Height: 0.73 m

Medium
Black granite

Technique
Rather soft, unsophisticated style

Condition
Good; the nose is slightly flattened; no trace of color

Provenance
Karnak *cachette*

Date
Ramses II (between Year 30 and Year 46)

Bibliography
Legrain, *Statues*, II, pl. XXIX, pp. 32, 33
Helck, *Verwaltung*, pp. 456-458
Kitchen, *Pharaoh Triumphant*, p. 178

When a temple was finally saturated with statues dedicated throughout the centuries, priests found themselves obliged to bury them in underground *cachettes*. There was no question of destroying them since they were sacred votive offerings. The largest number of monuments thus buried was found in a courtyard in Karnak; hundreds of masterpieces of stone and thousands of bronzes were uncovered.

Among the group were two statues of Vizier Khay. The one in granite is exhibited here. Sculpted in the attitude of a man crouching on a rounded cushion, his arms crossed on his knees, the right hand holding a head of lettuce, the vizier has a chapel in front of him. Only the façade is visible. The *naos* contains statuettes of Amon and the goddess Maat carved in the mass.

Khay's wig is made of locks falling in a fringe on the forehead, the sides free from the ears, thus showing the overhang behind the bows. The face, its features accentuated, is executed in a style which does not seem to suggest the finer studios of the capital.

From the inscriptions framing the chapel, decorating the back of the statue and surrounding the base, it is learned that the monument is dedicated to the god Amon-Re, lord of Karnak, and to the goddess Maat, sovereign of the gods, so that they will give Khay good and prosperous longevity.

The titles of this high civil servant of Ramses, whose two cartouches appear on the shoulders of the statue, reveal that Khay was, among other things, major-domo, royal scribe, first prophet of the goddess Maat, and especially mayor of the city and vizier. At times, the other known monuments of the vizier or those alluding to them refer to him not only as vizier of the South but also of the North. He succeeded Paser, one of Ramses' most famous viziers (cf. object 11), who, after serving Sethos I, began his career with his king at the age of 20, serving his master with fidelity and energy for 40 years.

The high duties of vizier had to be assumed with idealism and full impartiality, as the king always recalled on the day of enthronement. The duties covered the department of justice, the treasury, internal affairs, the armed forces, agriculture, government communications, etc. Furthermore, since he was in charge of Upper Egypt, the vizier regularly had to travel to Thebes where the community of craftsmen of the royal tomb had been placed under his immediate orders. Between years 30 and 46 of Ramses II, Khay was largely absorbed by the preparation and unfolding of the first five jubilees of Ramses–he celebrated 14 of them!–and helped Prince Khaemwaset, 12th son of the king who was primarily responsible for the jubilees. The most important evidence is preserved at Gebel Silsileh, south of Thebes in the grotto of King Haremhab. Like Paser, Khay ended his career with Pharaoh as a high priest of Amon and of Ptah. Neferronpet succeeded him as vizier.

Detail

Ramses, son of the solar miracle

To understand the full scope of any work of Egyptian art, the symbolism it expresses must be taken into account. Were it otherwise, the interpretation of this group composed of a chubby naked child with its finger in its mouth, crouched before a gigantic falcon, would be impossible. The infant, evoked in cosmic birth, is, however, the one his contemporaries called the "glorious sun of Egypt", the "mountain of gold and electrum", the "harvest of Egypt", the "perfect image of Re", the "chosen one of Re in the boat of the Sun", the "sun of princes", the "sun of all countries", the "powerful bull", the "one who makes foreign countries submit", the "great one of victories", the "lord of the Two Lands". . . and finally Usi-maa-re-Ra-mess(u)-meryamun, two last names of the five parts of his protocol which mean Powerful is the acting force of Re, the Chosen One of the Sun - the One the Sun brought into the world, Beloved of Amun. The Hittite sovereigns exchanging correspondence with Pharaoh translated these two names in their cuneiform writings into *Mashmouaria Shatepenria Réamashesha Mai-Amana!*

As was the case throughout the Middle East and for all of Antiquity, the attribution of a name, which then had to be protected, was essential to the individual since it gave him an identity and increased longevity, strengthened all the more when it was uttered aloud. First and foremost, this law applied to the king of Egypt whose "protocol" reflected the program of the reign. Certainly, Ramses was not the first pharaoh to go so far as to use the rebus system to translate his name in such a way as to prompt its reading given the strange aspect it may thereby have had. During the previous dynasty, the 18th, Queen Hatshepsut's favorite architect, Senenmut, transcribed the coronation name of his sovereign using very strange writing techniques. But if at that time, the rebus seems to have been used to pay poetic tribute to the queen, Ramses made it a principle which, through this artifice, enabled him to reinforce the divinity of his person; this was something of which he wished to convince all mortal beings. For this purpose, he dared use his own image. Thus, he is seen in the confines of Egyptian Nubia on the façade of the Great Temple of Abu Simbel, above the entranceway, appearing as a living play on words. His powerful human stature is endowed with the face of a falcon dominated by the sun (Re). Contemplating him, one recognizes the god Horus. But if the figure is more closely examined, it is noted that his hand rests on the sceptre with the head of a greyhound (*weser*) and that he dominates with his left hand the small statuette of the goddess of balance and of cosmic force (Maat). One then deciphers the phrase Usimaare, Ramses' coronation name.

At the northeastern boundary of the empire, in one of the sanctuaries of his capital, Pi-Ramses, he was aware of the fact that he was addressing natives, his contemporaries, but also foreign residents of the city—Semites who had mingled with the population as well as travellers arriving from the Middle East. To protect his body of the son of the god—or god incarnate himself—he chose Horon, the Semite, to whom he gave the shape of the falcon of Horus, the Sun of Egypt, thereby even suggesting that he was not only the offspring of the god but a divine concept which, despite his various appellations, constituted one and the same entity for distinct peoples.

Inspired by the initiatives undertaken early in the reign of Amenophis III during the previous dynasty, he even succeeded in treating his names as an object of offerings presented in tribute to the god, linking the creature with his creator. He also copied Amenophis III by having colossal monolithic statues, some taller than 20 metres, built with special names and tribute. This was one of the features of Ramses' policy: he took up the reforms instituted by his predecessors and exploited them for his own benefit through skillful modifications.

4

The god Horus watches over the child Ramses

Catalogue entry number in the Cairo Museum: 64,735

Dimensions
Height: 2.31 m
Length of the base: 1.33 m
Width of the base: 0.645 m

Medium
Grey granite; the falcon's face is of limestone.

Technique
In the sanctuary where it was found, the statue was attached by its tenon to a limestone base. The head of the falcon was resculpted in order to repair an old crack. The face has been restored.

Condition
Excellent. There is a small crack at the top of the plant.

Provenance
Tanis (San el-Hagar). Montet digs, 1934

Date
Ramses II

Bibliography

Montet, *Kémi 5* (1935), pp. 11-14, pl. X-XI
Montet-Bucher, *Revue biblique* 44 (1935), pp. 153-165, pl. V-VI
Montet, *Tanis* (1942), pp. 96-101, pl. IV
Montet, *Les énigmes de Tanis* (1952), pp. 73-74, pl. X
Montet, *L'Égypte et la Bible* (1959), p. 28, pl. II
Vandier, *Manuel* III, pp. 410, 419-20, pl. CXXXIII, 2
Muller, *Ägyptische Kunst* (1970), pl. 153
On the god Horus:
Stadelmann, *Syrisch-Palästinensische Gottheiten in Ägypten* (1967), pp. 76-88

Desroches Noblecourt *et alii*
Catalogue of the Ramsès le Grand exhibition, Paris, 1976, No. I, pp. 5-11

This massive composition of dark grey granite was found in 1934 by P. Montet in Tanis (western Delta) in a brick sanctuary against the surrounding wall of King Psusennes (first millennium BC). The group certainly came from Ramses' capital like most of the monuments of the great king which were transported from there to Tanis. As the inscription indicates, no other similar statue of colossal size is known showing Ramses II in that form and dominated by a god whose Egyptian appearance seems obvious, but to which a name of Semite origin—Horon—was given.

The falcon's face is of limestone. It has undoubtedly been restored but it also supports a covering of gold plating which would have given his solar face an intense luminosity. The base is part of the statue—a tenon on the upper part shows that the group was to have been fastened to a large foundation. Ramses is sculpted in the attitude of a child, his finger in his mouth. On his head is a sort of headband from which escape voluminous "childhood curls", fastened with a ribbon at the height of the ear. It is the image of the hieroglyph *mes*, which means "child". In his left hand, he holds the plant, symbolizing Upper Egypt, which is pronounced *su*. On his head—the forehead is adorned with the straight *uraeus*—is the sun which is pronounced *Ra*. The name of Ramessu, his name as a prince and the name by which his relatives called him at birth, is deciphered. The falcon, which has been placed behind the child, seems to welcome him into its lap. The two wings, so elegant and so prominent in their stylization, frame him to the shoulders. He is then taken up by the legs of the bird whose scales are marked with hatched incisions, the claws ending where the child is seated.

The essential features of the "peregrine falcon" are remarkably depicted though the stylization has neglected the masterly tiered arrangement of feathers on the shoulders and the elegant crossing of the wings, the right wing over the left, whose tips rest on the rectangular tail of the creature.

The inscription on the base tells us that this is the "god incarnate" Usimaare - Setepenre, Ramses-mery-Amun, beloved of Horus of (the city of) Ramses-mery-Amun.

There is evidence the Egyptians knew of the existence of this god of Semitic origin from the second millennium BC, a time when the god must have been worshipped not far from the site where Jerusalem was built. Appearing as one combatting everything that is evil, the god seems to have been introduced into Egypt during the reign of Amenophis II (middle of the 15th century BC). At that time, it was assimilated with the great sphinx of Giza, near which a temple was devoted to it. Among the various foreign divinities venerated by the Asiatic colonies living in Egypt—Anath, Astarte, Qadesh, Reshef, and Baal—this divine form may more readily be assimilated with Horus. In fact, it may be compared to the great sphinx Harmachis ("Horus of the horizon", ready to reappear on the horizon).

For Ramses, who so strongly wished to extend the political and religious borders of his country, such an object of syncretism could not be neglected.

It should be remembered, moreover, that the famous "Stele of Year 400", which was also erected in the vicinity of his capital (but which, after the capital was pillaged, was found at Tanis) reflects a similar concern on the part of the king: to recall that his ancestors hailed from this border region of Egypt and also that this region was, so to speak, linked to the god Seth, who, for the Egyptians until that time, had incarnated disorder. Early in the 19th dynasty, Seth had become the patron of the Ramesside family. To further stress this phenomenon which was compatible with his universalist spirit, Ramses had his image shown at the top of the "Stele of Year 400", offering vases of wine "to his father", the god Seth, who was represented, moreover, as the Asiatic Baal.

The family context

If one considers the royalty who preceded Haremhab,
the last pharaoh of the 18th dynasty, the list includes il-
lustrous names such as Hatshepsut, the world's first
great queen. Ramses, undoubtedly for very political
reasons, systematically omitted her, however, from the
list of his "official" ancestors of the very 18th dynasty
to which he referred. Nevertheless, probably no one
was unaware that he was a "Johnny-come-lately" in
the list of masters of Egypt. His father and grandfather
were not born of a "Great Royal Wife" but were viziers
of the last king of the 18th dynasty.

Two statues of the Vizier Pramesse, discovered
near the 10th pylon of Karnak, are particularly precious
since all evidence suggests the images of the paternal
grandfather of Ramses II are recognized in the statues.
Certainly, Pramesse had been the most important man
in the realm after the drama of Amarna. He had supported his sovereign in the struggle against those who
betrayed him (the event is recalled in a famous stele),
brought order to the administration and restored the
lost opulence of the Egyptian temples. His concerns
had not diminished the importance of the religious reforms which had just shaken the country. It was undoubtedly thanks to him that the famous "Book of the
Gates" was introduced into the funerary texts of his
sovereign. Sethos I, another vizier of Haremhab, succeeded the aged Pramesse, his father, who became
Ramses I and died a year and a half after his
coronation.

During the new reign–between years 13 and 15–
Sethos I completed the small funerary temple of his
father at Abydos, where the civil members of the royal
family are exceptionally seen attending the service.
Nearby, he built a sumptuous foundation with fine reliefs which even now are admired by the modern
world. The sovereign associated his son, the future
Ramses II, with power very early on. In the depths of
the Valley of the Kings, he had sculpted the most
majestic hypogeum, marvellously preserved to the
present day. His mother, Lady Sitre, was the first royal
lady, it would appear, to have been buried in the Valley
of the Queens. But it was for his wife, Tuya, who was
not of royal lineage either since she was the daughter
of a lieutenant-general of chariotry and her mother
was also of civilian origin, that Sethos I had a splendid
house of eternity built, rivalling in size and beauty that
of Nefertari, the favorite wife of his son, Ramses II. If
the monuments of the reign of Sethos I bring official
bas-reliefs to the acme of elegance which may be ad-

mired *in situ*, the effigies in the round of the king, on the other hand, are much more rare and none is sufficiently well-preserved to be loaned by the Cairo Museum to form part of this exhibition. As for the statues of Queen Tuya, they have been hammered and damaged to the point where it would be impossible to have a complete image of her face had we not discovered, in 1972, in the looted tomb of the queen, a "canopic" vase stopper sculpted in her effigy.

As has been established, Ramses' wives and children were innumerable but nothing equals in charm and beauty the representations of the Great Royal Wife Nefertari to whom he dedicated so many monuments and whose tomb even now has the best preserved paintings in the Valley of the Queens.

Bust of Tuya, mother of Ramses II

Journal of entries of the Luxor museum: J.191

Dimensions
Height (head and tenon): 0.17 m
Max. diameter of the head: 0.15 m
Diameter of the tenon: 0.11 m

Medium
Milky alabaster, formerly polychrome and inlaid

Technique
Sculpture in the round; inlaid pigments; traces of blue lapis lazuli on
the headdress; eyebrows and eyes originally inlaid with glass
(traces of mortar)

Condition
Almost perfect; neck and head of the vulture, eye and eyebrow inlays
missing; broken at the lower end of the right nostril;
polychrome almost totally gone.

Provenance
Western Thebes, Valley of the Queens, tomb of Queen Tuya (No. 80)

Date
Period of Ramses II

Bibliography
Desroches Noblecourt, *Temples de Nubie et de Thèbes*: Courrier du
CNRS, No. 9, July, 1973, pp. 36 and ff.

Desroches Noblecourt *et alii*
Catalogue of the Ramsès le Grand exhibition, Paris, 1976,
No. V, pp. 28-30
Desroches Noblecourt, *Touy, mère de Ramsès II, la reine Tanedjmy
et les reliques de l'expérience amarnienne*, Colloques
internationaux du CNRS, No. 595: L'Égyptologie en 1979,
Tome II, 1982, pp. 227-243.

Rare are the likenesses of Ramses' ancestors, but their quality is exceptional, as, for example, in this exquisite portrait of a woman who seemed to smile when she was discovered in March, 1972 at the lost site of the tomb of Tuya, mother of the king, in the Valley of the Queens. The bust is a stopper sculpted in the likeness of the queen. It closed one of the four canopic vases in which, as is known, the mummified viscera were placed. At that time still, it appears these stoppers, for reigning families, were sculpted in the likeness of their owners. Later, and especially in the case of civilians, the stoppers recalled the faces of the "four sons of Horus"–one with a human head, the three others evoking the heads of a dog, a baboon and a falcon.

Only the end of the queen's nose is chipped. The stopper also lacks the inlays of the eyebrows and eyes as well as those which would complete all the details of the feathers and the locks of hair of the headdress, though some traces of blue lapis lazuli powder still remain. The vulture and cobra heads which should stand on the forehead have been broken but at the top of the wig and on the sides remain engraved representations of the body and wings of the vulture which recall the state of "mother and Great Royal Wife". The claws of the bird hold the *shenu*, the sign of eternity.

The head dates to a turning-point in history when official art was strongly influenced by the best private workshops. It belonged to a lady aristocrat who entered the royal family through marriage. It is crowned with an almost civilian wig whose heavy locks are held at the height of the chin by a ribbon decorated with small rosettes. The wings of the vulture do not hang down, as in the following periods, on the locks framing the face, thereby making it possible to see the elements of the wig.

At the base of the neck appears the beginning of the "wide necklace". The second row, made of pearls in the shape of droplets, is distinguishable. Tuya's small square chin is strikingly found on the most accurate portraits of her son, Ramses. The great sovereign always showed infinite respect for the queen mother. He was no less attached to her. The façade of his majestic sanctuary at Abu Simbel portrays the king surrounded by his favorite wife, Nefertari, and the children of his other contemporary wives. But the latter do not appear on this façade. However, the likeness of his mother, called Mut-Tuya during her lifetime, or even Mut, was twice sculpted near her son.

She also appears with Nefertari in the Great Temple of the Ramesseum. The building, located north of the latter sanctuary, was long thought to be that of a temple dedicated to Sethos I. In reality, the ruins, as we were able to show in 1970, were those of the jubilee temple of Sethos, then Ramses, dedicated to Mut-Tuya, then to Nefertari, the two "favorite women" of the royal family.

When the queen mother died and passed into the world of eternity, it appears she could no longer ritually bear the name of Mut. Only the appellation Tuya remained assigned to her.

Religion, science and letters

Ramses always adopted an attitude of great diplomacy in regard to religion. All the main sanctuaries in his realm were revered and embellished. He made the entities venerated therein his own. In their arms or at their sides, he is one of them. He magnifies himself while minimizing, until it almost disappears, the distance separating the crown from the altar. During this period of syncretism, if ever there was one, he resumed the teachings of the reformer-king, Amenophis IV-Akhenaten. The tone, however, changed. Any god named was no longer unique, excluding all others. All the divine forms were, in reality, only the limbs of one and the same body and he was not far from representing the energies of the world in the form of the Living Sun, Great Breath (*shu*) of Egypt.

Amun-the-Hidden, who returned with the flooding of the Nile and who brought all life back to Egypt, remained the undisputed lord of Thebes and continued to protect the king. The great festivals were respected, the processions honored and the sphinxes of the god or the king bordered the *dromo*s. The treasures and votive offerings accumulated in his great enclosure, in the reign of Ramses III, would even total 5,164 divine images and 86,486 praying statues.

However, the masses dared implore Amun-the-Judge-of-the-Poor who would intervene as the vizier (!), the "ferryman of the poor", the "bulwark of the thousands". He was called upon as the "bronze gate", the "pilot". The king, his intercessor, ordered Bakenkhons, high priest of Amun, to have the "temple of Ramses-meryamun-who-hears-prayers" built east of Karnak. An opening made in the courtyard of the building allowed the devout to perceive a miraculous colossus of the sovereign behind a balustrade. In short, Ramses had initiated his people into a religion of faith different from that which dominated their beliefs about the hereafter.

The exhibition hall is dominated by the statue of May, Ramses' architect who worked wonders in the king's new capital. The architects were among the most scholarly of all the scribes and their reputation has come down through the centuries, culminating in the "beatification" of some among them.

The statue of another very famous scribe, exhibited in the following section, was chosen, though he came after the reign of Ramses II, for his unequalled grace and the position which the baboon evoking Thoth, patron of science and letters, occupies between his head and shoulders. Other statues contemporary with the son of Sethos show a similar composition, the ape appearing in the round as if one sought to locate the seat of thoughts, functioning under the protection and control of the supreme intelligence.

In the Ramesside period, Egypt experienced intense intellectual activity. The king fostered erudition, constantly referring to the most important scientific institution in the country, the "houses of life" and, more specifically, the "house of books" where he himself went to consult the most confidential archives and to know "the hidden things of the sky and all the secrets of the earth". Scribes in the houses copied the most varied books (rolls of papyrus); laboratories operated, visited by surgeons, physicians as well as pharmacists. The experiments in these premises were more closely related to empirical science than to magic. The school of medicine was highly considered. People came from Syria to consult Egyptian practitioners. An Egyptian physician, it will be recalled, was sent to the ailing Hittite princess.

Weights, measures, maps of the sky, Books of the Nile, the key to dreams were placed in these "houses of life" and the scribes "who received the writing-desk"—a sort of bachelor's degree—had access to them.

Under Ramses, neo-Egyptian, close to the spoken language and introduced into the texts of the court beginning with Amenophis IV, had replaced classical Egyptian. The adoption of syllabic writing made it possible to include in the vocabulary many words of foreign origin, borrowed from highly diverse peoples with whom the Egyptians had come into contact. Interpretation schools existed while in Pharaoh's harem, in Fayum at Mi-Wer, the great ladies instructed some young foreigners who had been entrusted to them for training.

All the genres of literature flourished—poetry with a romantic tendency to nature, scepticism, epic poems, folk tales and even love songs which, in intensity, equalled their eastern counterpart, the Song of Songs.

Humor, irony and satire were fully accepted. But the libraries also contained the prestigious list of the pharaohs as well as geographical maps. For Ramses, all was adapted to the propaganda of the royal religion. Those who studied the march of the stars and the apparent course of the sun in the sky worked with architects to design sanctuaries in the image of the cosmos and to give them life through divine inspiration.

At the Ramesseum, the jubilee temple of Ramses, a ceiling showing the calendar concurring with the known data of astronomy was surrounded with so many complements, including the famous "golden circle", that Diodorus of Sicily (I,49) still spoke of it when he visited this "tomb of Osymandias", the altered name of Usimaare.

More specifically, it is the sun altar of Abu Simbel, miraculously preserved, which makes it possible to suggest, in its broad lines, the significance of the rites which were celebrated to ensure the continuity of the diurnal and nocturnal cycle.

In addition, the archives of the "house of life" revealed to Ramses (inscription on the pylon of Luxor) that Thebes, the Heliopolis of the south, "was the right eye of Re" and that the left "was the nome of the Heliopolis of the North". Here, therefore, were the two great cities of Amun and Re, twinned in this celestial regard consisting of the moon and the sun, the night and the day succeeding each other. It is the manner of writing Eternity in hieroglyphs. In a word, Amun-Re is the Eternal.

In the great temple of Abu Simbel, the sun, on two occasions during the year (February 20 and October 20), still penetrates to the back, completely illuminating three of the four statues of the sanctuary. Pharaoh and the Eternal are but one. He is the sun-king!

6

Statue of May, one of Ramses' greatest architects

Catalogue entry number in the Cairo Museum: 67,878

Dimensions
Total height: 0.74 m
Base
Height: 0.115 m
Width: 0.385 m
Depth: 0.473 m

Medium
Grey granite

Technique
Single block; archaistic sculpture

Condition
Very good

Provenance
Kôm el-Qalâa, near Mit Rahineh

Date
Ramses II. The figure also lived under Merenptah.

Bibliography
Sauneron, *Le chef des travaux Mây*, BIFAO 53 (1953), pp. 57-63
Labib Habachi, *Grands personnages en mission ou de passage à
        Assouan, I. Mey, attaché au temple de Rê*, CdE 29
        (1954), pp. 210-220, figs. 27-28
Gaballa, *Some Nineteenth Dynasty Monuments in the Cairo
        Museum 1
        A New Monument of May, Chief of Works*, BIFAO 71 (1972),
        pp. 129-133, pl. XXIII-XXV

Desroches Noblecourt *et alii*
        Catalogue of the Ramsès le Grand exhibition, 1976

The statue shows a man squatting, both hands flat on his knees, palms facing upwards, waiting to receive offerings. He wears a wig which flares out at the shoulders and whose tips are pointed at each side of the neck. The wig is made of hair with wavy locks, indicated by vertical ridges beginning at the top of the head and further apart at the shoulders. Horizontal waves slightly in relief start at the top of the ears; the latter are large and clearly defined.

The face, with slightly closed, almond-shaped eyes, has a rather prominent brow. The nose is rounded and the mouth, small and tight-lipped. The chin is short, but heavy, and covered with a small beard. The whole of the physiognomy gives the impression of a person of subtle, organized cunning. His attitude is that of extreme simplicity—exceedingly humble before his god, whose benediction he seems to await. His clothing and his hair are no more affected and do not indicate the fashion of the times. A curved line at the base of the neck would suggest he is wearing a shirt but there is no trace of sleeves on the arms. A long loincloth stops at the waist. The two flaps of the material overlap in front. The upper edges, tucked in against the abdomen, are naturally pleated by this movement in a sort of lateral projection. The tip of the left flap may be seen, forming a lapel. The flap passes across the entire front of the figure, covered with an inscription made up of six horizontal lines. The elbows are rather angular and the forearms, stiff. The robe is slightly curved between the two knees it covers. The shoulders are somewhat sloped but the form of the chest seems to blend with a torso whose muscles are tired and where there are folds of a paunch. The shape of the back, on the other hand, is rather pure and elegant. The man is seated on a base rounded at the rear.

The inscription engraved between his hands is a prayer to the god of Memphis, Ptah, the "Lord of Justice", asking him, to give life, health and prosperity to May, identified as the chief of works in the temples of Re and Ptah and chief of the craftsmen in the Great Palace of the Prince, at Heliopolis. Son of Chief of Works Bakenamun, his grandparents were the Chief Chancellor Nebiot and Lady Takartia.

The style of the statue recalls that found in some monuments of the Middle Kingdom. Indeed, it has even been suggested that this is a likeness dating to that period. However, certain stylistic details point to a monument executed in keeping with archaism, expressing the intentional simplicity which certain architects sought to give their monuments.

May's career unfolded during the reign of Ramses II and drew to a close during that of Ramses' son and successor, Merenptah, whose two names are engraved on the figure's shoulders.

Various traces of this figure have reached us. The statue was found by chance near the temple of Merenptah in the ruins of ancient Memphis.

The architect must have lived a long time since the information available about him indicates he was chief of works for all the monuments in Ramses' capital. It is known that an enormous quantity of granite was used to construct these religious buildings. Inscriptions at Aswan and on the island of Sehel provide evidence of expeditions to the quarries. It is assumed he could have used some blocks of granite from the pyramids at Giza but some doubt persists if one considers the care Ramses and his son Khaemwaset lavished on the relics of the ancient kings. May even dedicated a stele to the great Sphinx in addition to the monuments he mentioned in the inscription on his statue.

It was apparently natural that he should participate in the building of the temple of Merenptah in Memphis.

7

The scribe Ramsesnakht dominated by the baboon of Thoth

Catalogue entry number in the Cairo Museum: 36,582
Cairo general catalogue: 42,162

Dimensions
Height: 0.75 m
Width: 0.43 m
Depth: 0.39 m

Medium
Grey granite

Condition
Excellent

Provenance
Eastern Thebes, Karnak, *cour de la cachette* (found in 1904)

Date
Ramses IV - Ramses VI

Bibliography
Legrain, *Statues*, II, pl. XXVI, p. 29
Legrain, *ASAE VI* (1905), pp. 133-134
Lefebvre, *Grands Prêtres*, pp. 178-180, 263 (28 a)
Helck, *Verwaltung*, pp. 381, 493-494
Vandier, *Manuel* III, pl. CL, pp. 533-534
Cerny, *CAH* II, XXXV (Cambridge, 1965), pp. 23-25
Porter-Moss II (1972), p. 146
Almagro, *Arte faraonico* (Madrid-Barcelona, 1975)

Desroches Noblecourt *et alii*
Catalogue of the Ramsès le Grand exhibition, 1976,
    No. XXXII, pp. 136-137

The image of the scribe alone evokes a major part of Egyptian culture, science and religious thought transmitted through sites and centuries.

Beginning with the reign of Ramses II, a new type of scribe statue appeared, influenced by the well-known image of the time of Amenophis III. In the latter, the likeness of the crouching intellectual writes under the protection of the baboon of Thoth perched in front of or beside him. Under Ramses II, a new step was taken: the ape, symbolizing the intelligence, restraint, exactness, and knowledge which gave man his grandeur, appeared perched on the head of the scholar. When the ape is not seen in relief, it is engraved on the sides of the wig, as is the case with a statue at the Musée du Louvre.

The scribe Ramsesnakht dates to the reign of Ramses IV and his two successors, but he continues to evoke a form introduced under the great king. All the intellect of the erudite takes shape in this animal in continuous movement which seems to indicate the brain as the seat of thought processes. The creation is typical of the reign of Ramses II.

Ramsesnakht, dressed in the fashion of the period with his pleated skirt and wide, three-quarter sleeves, has a paunch, indicating he is portrayed during the second part of his life. The inscription unrolled on his knees refers to his career. We thus learn he was a high priest of Amun.

Catalogue entry number in the Cairo Museum: 37,525

Dimensions
Ext. height: 0.35 m
Int. height: 0.326 m
Upper ext. diameter: 0.49 m
Max. lower diameter: 0.275 m
Thickness of the rim: 0.02 m

Medium
Alabaster, opaque turquoise blue glass paste, cornelian

Technique
Deeply incised to hold incrustation

Condition
A real restoration puzzle. Numerous missing parts filled in with
    plaster. Restored in 1976.

Provenance
Eastern Thebes, Temple of Karnak, *cour de la cachette*

Date
Late 18th dynasty: Amenophis III (1417-1379 BC)

Bibliography
Daressy, *Deux clepsydres antiques*, in *BIE*, Series 5, 9 (1915), pp. 5-16
Borchardt, *Zeitmessung*, pp. 6-7, pl. 1-3
Sloley, *Ancient Egypt*, 1924, pp. 43-50; *Primitive Methods of
    Measuring Time*, in *JEA* 17 (1931), pp. 174-176
Parker, *The Calendars of Ancient Egypt*, Chicago, 1950, p. 40
Neugebauer and Parker, *Egyptian Astronomical Texts III*,
    London, 1969

Desroches Noblecourt *et alii*
Catalogue of the Ramsès le Grand exhibition, Paris, 1976, No. XXXIII,
    pp. 138-149

This is the first water "watch"—the first known clock in the world. The notion of sun dials and gnomons certainly already existed but only to indicate the hours of the day with the help of the sun. At night, however, the moon could not take over.

The Egyptians established the first sun calendar. It was so perfectly simple that Julius Caesar adopted it with minimal changes. The 365-day year was composed of 12 months of 30 days to which were added five supplementary days which the Greeks called "epagomenal days". The quarter day was not neglected; it introduced an extra day every four years.(The Egyptian *civil* calendar did not accept this but the priests in the temples were not mistaken.)

The month was divided into three weeks of ten days (the decades) and the days into 24 diurnal and nocturnal hours. Since everything was based on the brightness of the sun and its presence among men, each of the 24 hours took different proportions according to the seasons. In Summer, the hours of the day were longer and the nocturnal hours, shorter and vice versa. The pattern of the Egyptian climate was such that the months, instead of breaking down into four equal series of three divisions, were grouped in three seasons of four months each. The year began in Egypt when flooding occurred around July 18 of the Julian calendar and was marked by three consecutive events—the return of the star Sothis, which disappeared from the Egyptian sky for 75 days; this appearance virtually coincided with the sunrise and within a few degrees of where the star came into view. These phenomena were then followed by the surging of the flood. The first season of the year thus covered four months. It was the *akhit* season. The parched earth of Egypt was again covered with an immense body of water and came to life again. The Spring-Winter season followed; fields were sown and growing was supervised.

The hours of the night appeared longer during the period. Such was the *perit* season when vegetation grew. It was succeeded by the four months of *shemu*, the origin of the word *hama(m)*. It ended with intense heat, following the harvest, when the earth cracked with drought and all life seemed hopeless until the Nile miraculously returned once again.

This calendar set the tempo of the daily and seasonal existence of the Egyptians and is reflected in a multitude of occurrences. The organization of the water clock takes these various aspects into consideration. Inside, graduations are marked with small staggered dots on twelve vertical lines ending at each month of the three seasons. Their intervals vary slightly according to the period. The vessel, which was filled with water, was shaped in the form of a truncated cone. The small base located in the lower portion allowed the liquid to escape through a hole. Water pressure was strongest when the vessel was filled. A greater quantity of water had to flow, therefore, for the surface of the liquid to drop by one degree. As the clock emptied, one could read the various hours by checking the level reached by the surface of the water inside.

In fact, eleven stages were marked by small dots which ended at the base in an *ankh* or a *djed* sign, since the first hour corresponded to the surface line on the inside upper portion of the clock.

The clepsydra presented here, sculpted in alabaster and found in the humid basement of the Karnak *cachette*, lay in pieces and has been remarkably restored. Glass paste and cornelian incrustations still remain. The object dates to the time of Amenophis III and is included in the exhibition for a major reason— the famous astronomical ceiling of the jubilee temple of Ramses II, the Ramesseum, fully concurs with the Egyptian calendar which runs clockwise, engraved on the clepsydra. In addition, this example of the Amenophis III period was analyzed by astronomers who, after studying the scenes with Egyptologists, observed that they did not express the calendar of the *civil* year (it lost one day every four years) of the time of Amenophis III. However, its readings matched the position of the stars in the Egyptian sky between 1630 and 1510 BC. This evidence clearly corroborates the text which tells us the clepsydra was invented by a certain Amenemhat who lived between the reigns of Ahmose and Tuthmosis I. The illustrations are therefore a copy of the original object and its outer decoration is consequently purely symbolic.

Detail

The clepsydra is divided into three sections. The lower section is made up of six scenes, each evoking two months per season. They symmetrically frame the opening through which the liquid escapes. The liquid is visible in the projection formerly ornamented with the image of a seated baboon. The water flowed through the phallus. When the scenes recall flooding, the sovereign is shown offering vessels of wine to male or female divinities. The following period of the year–two scenes–is illustrated by the king's adoration of the god of genetic heat which makes plants grow, namely the ityphallic Min. The middle of this period, i.e., the sixth month of the year, is illustrated by a standing hippopotamus. The name of *great flame* is given to it; it is the zenith of Winter. Another hippopotamus following the first bears the name of *small flame*, the phase when Winter draws to a close to make way for the last month of the year which, with the festival of the goddess Renenutet, announces the harvest.

An important observation to be made is the fact that in the Mesopotamian calendar, the *great flame* and the *small flame* are also mentioned. It should be noted that the two last scenes depicting the Summer season in which the two falcon gods are venerated by the king express the period when the sun shines intensely until the other side is reached of the device through which the water flows.

The central scene in the middle section, in the axis of the hole of evacuation, refers especially to Ursa Major, symbolized by a bull whose body takes the form of an oval.

In the third section, in the same axis, is Isis-Sothis introducing the first 30 days of the flooding season, illustrated by a slim goddess standing on a ship, her right arm raised behind her head, crowned with two long feathers. In front of her, the skiff of Orion actually precedes her–it is the fourth month of the Summer season. The two other barques without rudder or oars, shown behind that of the goddess, are occupied by the king, accompanied successively by the planets Jupiter and Saturn. Further in this direction, the planet Saturn is mentioned and Venus is evoked in the form of the Phoenix. In the late Egyptian period, the clepsydra system was improved. The truncated cone was replaced by a cylindrical form then filled with a drip which was checked. The flow was constant and the hours were more precise. Unlike the Karnak clepsydra exhibited here, the reading was then made from bottom to top.

It should be recalled the Romans adopted this system: to measure the time a lawyer could speak, he was given a certain water time (*aquam dare*). Cicero was not altogether the honest lawyer described in literature for, in order to have additional time to plead his case, he did not hesitate to mix sand with the water of the court's clepsydra!

Scribe's palette

Catalogue entry number in the Cairo Museum: SR 305 = C.69,033

Dimensions
Length: 0.323 m
Width: 0.06 m

Medium
Schist

Provenance
Tell el-Roubea (?)

Date
Subsequent to the New Kingdom

Bibliography
(cf. N.B. at the bottom of the technical data for object 40)
Desroches Noblecourt, *Le papyrus. Le matériel des scribes*,
    in La Feuille Blanche, Paris, 1942, No. 4 and No. 5
Barquet, *Le Livre des Morts des Anciens Egyptiens*, Paris, 1967,
    Chap. 94

The "scribe who had received the writing-desk" may be viewed, all things considered, as a bachelor degree graduate today. In short, he had completed his secondary studies and could be assigned to an administration, to an army officers' school or to one of the temples' Houses of Life to pursue further studies.

The palette given the scribe had to be of lightweight wood and very manageable. In the Old Kingdom, it was rather massive and was sometime accompanied by two large independent bowls for ink. In the New Kingdom, however, the typical writing-desk was most often a strip with a depression at the centre for several *calami*, or small brushes, with which to write. They were made of reeds and were not bevelled like the famous goose quills of the past. At the top of the palette, two hollows each contained cakes of solidified red and black ink.

From the start, the other accessories required for writing were placed in a small leather bag closed with a slide. In it, the scribe naturally carried his cakes of spare ink, a small, very fine sandstone erasing-block, a smoothing tool to repair the surface of the papyrus he had "erased" and a small bowl of water. A long case could be added to this equipment to hold spare reeds. The scribe working in a ministry no longer wrote on pottery or limestone shards—the *ostraca* on which he did his exercises—but on wooden palettes or long rolls of papyrus consisting of several pages pasted together or sometimes even on parchment.

The rolls were kept in rectangular chests with small legs, topped with a cornice and often painted red, black or white. The covers of the chests could take the form of a desk.

The palette exhibited here is votive, meaning it was placed in a burial vault for strictly funerary purposes. In fact, the medium of which it is made –schist– is not sufficiently manageable. In addition, the object has no container for *calami*, and with good reason.

Its "archaistic" forms prompt dating to the Saitic period. Its presence in the tomb fulfils the wishes of the deceased who, in order to overcome the trials he faces, must have, according to Chapter 94 of the Book of the Dead, "this pen-box of Thoth and the secrets related to it".

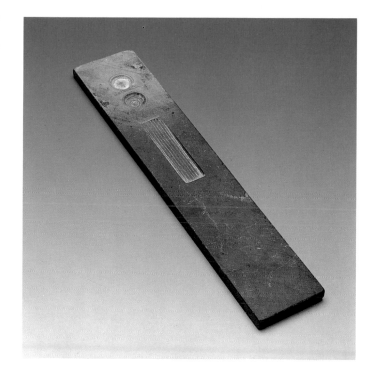

Special Cairo register: 11,775
Temporary catalogue entry number in the Cairo Museum: 14-6-24-20

Dimensions
Max. height: 1.02 m
Min. height: 0.82 m
Max. width: 1.17 m
Min. width: 0.68 m

Medium
Formerly polychrome sandstone

Technique
Intaglio engraved relief

Condition
Fragmentary blocks

Provenance
Western Thebes, Asasif, Theban tomb of a nobleman

Date
19th dynasty

Bibliography
Encyclopédie photo, p. 28, pl. No. 149

Desroches Noblecourt *et alii*
Catalogue of the Ramsès le Grand exhibition, Paris, 1976, No. XXIV,
    pp. 110-113

The two blocks, decorated almost identically, come from an anonymous tomb located in the western massif of Thebes called Asasif. Looted in the 19th century, the tomb yielded other sculpted fragments now in the archaeological museum of Florence.

The ensemble bears all the marks of Ramesside art and must date to the end of Ramses' reign. The lower and upper sections deal with an official ceremony. The dignitaries–the hems of their long robes may be seen–are important figures in the ceremonial costume. The middle section, the best preserved, shows, at left, the first part of the parade introduced by two viziers with shaved heads, wearing robes characteristically starched in front, held by two straps tied at the back of the neck. One of the figures carries the *flabellum* which places him "to the right of the king". On his arm, the great ceremonial scarf is also tied. It holds the hook, the insignia of the South which Pharaoh and the viceroy of Nubia may have wished to have on hand. Behind them, in four rows, are the lords in their wide tunics with puffed sleeves, all wearing long black winged wigs. They parade in hurried rows as if they do not want to lose precious time. They hold a papyrus rolled at the ends, long canes, a round-bodied vessel and a cabbage lettuce. Bare-footed viziers and courtiers are bowed since they must certainly be approaching the sovereign. In the rear, despite a crack in the sandstone, may be seen a servant, perhaps belonging to the clergy since his head is shaven, who carries a pile of offering tables on which are placed "reward necklaces" with two rows, wider, open neckpieces with two fastening cords, a stemmed bowl and numerous cups. The parade is surely heading for a ceremony at which decorations are to be awarded and various donations made, such as those evoked in tombs from the time of King Amenophis IV. On such occasions, the king would appear at a window, alone or escorted by some members of his family and, from the balcony, would throw a wide variety of objects found on the stool shown at the left of the relief. He could add, for example, red leather gloves, similar to those presented by Amenophis IV-Akhenaten to his chief of chariotry, the divine father Ay.

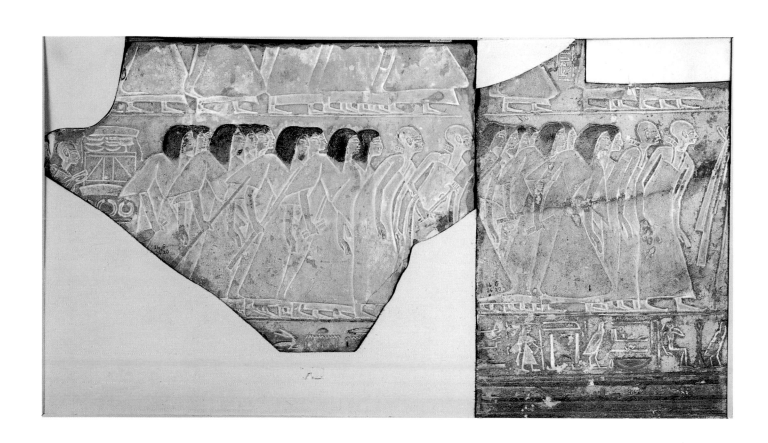

11

Procession of the boat
of Amun during the Feast
of the Valley

Catalogue entry number in the Cairo Museum: 43,591

Dimensions
Height: 0.60 m (approx.)
Length: 0.80 m (approx.)

Medium
Painted limestone; white and yellow background; red flesh and wigs; white clothing; vestiges of blue and green on the boats and *flabella*

Technique
Bas-relief decoration; intaglio engraved texts

Condition
Broken into two pieces; a fragment is missing in the lower left portion; cleaned in 1976

Provenance
Western Thebes; Deir el-Medina (in the enclosure of the temple, at the southwestern corner)

Date
Ramses II

Bibliography
Porter-Moss I 2, p. 669
Baraize, *Compte-rendu des travaux éxécutés à Deir el-Médineh*, *ASAE* 13 (1913), pp. 36, 41
Foucart, *Un temple flottant. Le vaisseau d'or d'Amon-Râ*, *Monuments Piot* 25 (1921-22), p. 165, Fig. 6
Foucart, *La Belle fête de la Vallée*, BIFAO 24 (1924), p. 103, pl. XI

Family aspect of the festival
Schott, *Das schöne Fest vom Wüstentale*, Wiesbaden, 1953

Desroches Noblecourt *et alii*
Catalogue of the Ramsès le Grand exhibition, Paris, 1976, No. XXVII, pp. 124-127

The relief, still bearing traces of polychrome, was found in the enclosure of the temple at Deir el-Medina. It dates to the period of Ramses II. Its main subject, on the upper section, is composed of the small divine procession boat of the god Amun before which Ramses, dressed in a long, sumptuous robe of pleated linen with a rigid jewelled "apron" and wearing a small wig with curls and royal serpent, but without his crown, officiates with a disked, falcon-headed censer. On the low flames of the burner, held with one hand, he throws balls of incense.

Prow and stern are adorned with two rams' heads, the sacred animal of the god Amun, topped with the sun disk. The necklaces on the necks of the rams could have been gold. On the deck of the divine ark may be seen a royal sphinx standing on its hind legs, the images of the goddesses Maat and Hathor and that of the crouching sovereign who presents offerings and holds up the small columns of the divine cabin. The latter is shrouded by a veil decorated with spirits protecting the idol. The veil was drawn back at the stations of the ship in the harbor which marked its procession, enabling spectators to admire the incarnation of the god contained in the portable sanctuary. On the hull of the ship are three small kneeling spirits with falcon heads evoking the lands at the lowest levels of the Delta, at Buto. On the other side, similar spirits with dog heads symbolized the highest regions of the land in the south of Egypt, at Hieraconpolis. The ship rests on four heavy shafts supported by six rows of priests, three under the stern, three on the prow, for a total of 24 officiating figures in priestly garb, their heads shaven, wearing billowing, pleated robes with flaps falling in front.

On the side of the boat, two priests garbed in cheetah skins accompany the sacred procession. In front of them, a man turns, holding two *flabella*, one in the shape of an ostrich plume, the other ending in a fan suggesting a lotus flower. The name engraved above his head reveals he is Ipuy, very likely the chief sculptor of the workers at Deir el-Medina, ordered by Pharaoh to dig and decorate the royal tombs. It is known the workmen, assembled in corporations, played a major part in the celebrations of the beautiful "Festival of the Valley" late in the 10th month of the Egyptian year when Summer had begun. It was a panegyric with the temple of Karnak as a starting point. The great boat of the god called *Woserhat*, which could measure up to 130 cubits (about 67 metres) and

which was plated with gold, encrusted with precious materials, and enhanced by an impressive number of figurines and a pair of small obelisks, left Amun's sanctuary. Slipping through canals and the river, the barque brought with it the procession boat of the god seen here. Then carried on men's backs, the boat was to visit the gods of the West, i.e., the dead pharaohs on the left bank of Thebes in the sovereigns' temples of "millions of years". The procession travelled to all these sanctuaries, ending at the temple of Hathor at Deir el-Bahri.

The relief fragment exhibited here shows one of the wayside altars with a side torus, marked with the name of Ramses and dominated by a cornice. The boat appears to be emerging from it, followed by the vizier of Upper Egypt, Paser, who holds the *flabellum* here. Behind him, in miniature, appears Amenemope, the famous figure of the village of Deir el-Medina– scribe of the craftsmen of the royal tomb–with a papyrus bouquet. Craftsmen specially assigned to the Valley of the Kings and the Valley of the Queens naturally took a major part in this ceremony in honor of deceased sovereigns.

On the lower section of the bas-relief remain the vestiges of the prow of the celebrated boat *Woserhat*, in very small scale, its ram's head decorated with the great *Atef* crown. The boat, after docking at the edge of the canal perpendicular to the Nile, crossed the entire fertile plain of the western bank. At the close of festivities, the god's ark was returned to the temple of Karnak. The traditional visits to the Western tombs were followed by funerary meals in the sanctuaries of the private burial places and ritual drinking sessions, which gave rise to euphoria. They sought to bring about the return of the spirit of the deceased. The crouching figure in front of the prow of the *Woserhat* is Amenemope himself. His prayer is materialized by seven vertical columns on which he addresses Amun-Re: "the Primeval, He who came into Existence the First, the Unique . . . He who made the Sky, the Earth, the Waters" . . . "Come to me, Amun . . . make me reach the boundary of the desert: come to me, Amun, He who saves the castaway . . . Help me reach the West."

12

Pair of clappers

Catalogue entry number of the Cairo Museum: 25,820

Dimensions
Length: 0.175 m

Medium
Bone (?)

Technique
Each is made of a single piece.

Condition
Good

Provenance
Thebes

Date
New Kingdom

Bibliography
(Cf. *Nota bene* at the bottom of technical data of 40)
Heckmann, Catalogue général . . . du Musée du Caire, *Les instruments de musique,* Cairo
Ziegler, *Catalogue des instruments de musique du musée du Louvre,* Paris, 1979

This type of instrument was generally made of the bone or ivory of large mammals. Most of the time, the form is straight. Clappers not designed for common use but assigned to the highest ceremonial purposes before the very essence of femininity—the goddess Hathor—were more luxurious and especially sculpted in elephant tusks which gave them their curved form. They always followed the line of the forearm; the latter could be adorned with bracelets. The hand at the end of the arm was fitted into the head of the goddess Hathor who had cow ears. The clappers were used by Hathor worshippers during ritual dances and the cult of festival days (cf. relief 11) during which worshippers chanted as in some religious celebrations today. The movement was naturally rather slow since the two parts of the clappers were held together by an element which passed through two holes intended for this purpose at the height of the elbow.

The object exhibited here has the simplest form, consisting of straight forearms ending in hands with outstretched fingers unadorned with rings. A bracelet on each wrist is suggested by six incised lines.

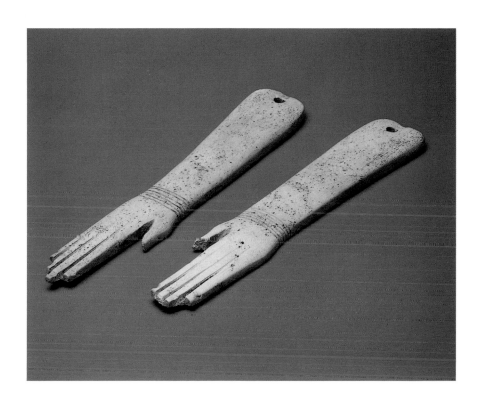

13

Study of an image of the ram of Amun

Provisional Cairo Museum number: 23-2-22-1

Dimensions
Total height: 0.11 m
Width: 0.18 m

Medium
Limestone chip

Technique
Black and red drawing

Condition
Broken and restored

Provenance
Western Thebes, Valley of the Kings

Date
Merenptah-Ramses III

Bibliography
Forman-Kischkewitz, *Die Altägyptische Zeichnung*,
  (Prague, 1971), No. 9
Černy, *A Community of Workmen at Thebes*, IFAO Bibliothèque
  d'Étude, T. 50 (Cairo, 1973), p. 125

Desroches Noblecourt *et alii*
Catalogue of the Ramsès le Grand exhibition, Paris, 1976,
  No. XXIX, pp. 130-131

This limestone fragment, an *ostracon* found in the Valley of the Kings, was certainly drawn by one of the decorator workers of the royal hypogea. Digs in the village of Deir el-Medina, where generations of craftsmen of the royal necropolis succeeded one another from the beginning of the New Kingdom, produced, besides precious rolls of papyrus with historical texts, school textbooks and even a book on dream interpretation, other more humble vestiges such as small sheets used by oracles or for draws and a great quantity of magnificent limestone chips the color of ivory on which were inscribed pages of writing (corrected by the school master!), attendance sheets of workers and all sorts of freely drawn sketches close to the subjects nature supplied and which were then stylized to decorate the walls of rock-cut tombs.

Here one sees the quite naturalistic image of a prone ram, its legs folded under it, the horns curved, symbolizing the sacred animal of the god Amun. Its silhouette is repeated *ad infinitum* in the alleys of the sphinx of Karnak where it also appears with rounded horns. The ram may readily be confused with the ram of the potter-god Khnum of Elephantine, which had horizontal, undulated horns. Its image is shown in the horizontal line of hieroglyphs dominating the papyrus.

Above a basket covered with leaves is a flower and a lotus bud with a round bread and a large fig on the front. Certainly, the Egyptians were never animal worshippers and it would not appear the ram of Amun was considered a god. But the ardors of the creator could be expressed and illustrated by those of the leader of the flock–the divine spark dwelled in animal; it was sacred.

The style, perhaps slightly less sophisticated than that of the time of Ramses II, particularly in the detail of the plants, instead indicates the genre of the period of Ramses III. There is confirmation in the vertical line of hieroglyphs drawn at the back of the animal. It mentions the chief of works Hay, who was well-known in the village of Deir el-Medina. He had lived during the reign of the conqueror of the Peoples of the Sea.

14

Study for illustration of the singing harpist

Catalogue entry number of the Cairo Museum: 69,409

Dimensions
Total height: 0.138
Width: 0.11 m

Medium
Limestone chip

Technique
Black and red drawing

Condition
Lower part destroyed

Provenance
Western Thebes, Deir el-Medina

Date
In the style of the Ramesside period

Bibliography
Vandier d'Abbadie, *Ostraca figurés de Deir el-Médineh*, Vol. III
    (Cairo, 1946), p. 158, Pl. XCIV

Desroches Noblecourt *et alii*
Catalogue of the Ramsès le Grand exhibition, Paris, 1976,
    No. XXX, pp. 132-133

The famous "Song of the Harpist" would seem to be the only note one is accustomed to interpreting as "pessimistic" in all the Egyptian funerary texts which, if one had followed the "way of God" and if the weighing of earthly actions was favorable to the deceased, promised him blessed Eternity.

However, two writings dating to the period of Ramses II, found in the tomb of his vizier Paser and in the vault of one of the craftsmen of the necropolis, Anhurkhaw, leave some doubt as to or at least underline the inescapable character of separation after death between the living and the dead. Here are a few passages: "Since the time of the god (bodies were created to depart, others to replace them) . . . Make a joyous day, O Paser! Forget what is evil, think of happiness, until the day of death comes, since fate does not stop counting the days and nothing may be added to what has been calculated for you. Among those who have departed, no one has ever returned . . . Make a joyous day! Place before you frankincense and oil, adorn your chest with lotus and flowers . . . the women you love seated next to you."

This song is illustrated by the image of a harpist who is often crouching, sometimes standing, as is the case here. Some representations imply the harpist is always blind. He plucks some of the 12 strings of his instrument. The harp was typically Egyptian and its evolution and the amplification of its forms may be noted from the period of the pyramids. The specimen shown here is large in size as it later was in the West. The pegs holding the strings are alternately red and black. Its sound box is often covered with leather-colored scallops. (The large harp in the Musée du Louvre is decorated with pink and light green leather.) The harpist wears a large robe with wide sleeves. His head is apparently bald, as always, and is adorned with a colored headband. Rolls of fat are suggested on the neck of the musician.

A magnificent example figured in the tomb of Ramses III.

When this type of figure appears on the walls of tombs in the Middle Kingdom, the texts it illustrates take a much more poignant turn. They have been accused of pessimism and likely serve as a demonstration of the famous *carpe diem* which encourages man to take full advantage of life, not knowing what awaits him on the other side. However, it may be useful to shade this judgment. The storyteller should not be assigned such materialistic reasoning which, in fact, would be incompatible with Egyptian religious philosophy. The phrase "Make a joyous day" certainly applies to funerary rites given the sound of the harp and the gestures of the dancers accompanying it, mainly those of the acrobatic figure on the bridge–an incitement to divine love. After having impregnated the great goddess, the deceased, who awaited eternal rebirth, had to undergo a long "purgatory" whose trials and detours were unknown to him in advance notwithstanding the Book of the Dead which he brought with him.

15

Satirical papyrus with animal scenes

Catalogue entry number of the Cairo Museum: 31,199

Dimensions
Max. height: 0.13 m
Total length: 0.555 m

Medium
Papyrus and mineral colors

Technique
Pasted pellicular fibers of papyrus stems; black, red and yellow ochre, grey-blue and white paint

Condition
Fragmentary

Provenance
Unknown

Date
Ramesside period

Bibliography
Brunner-Traut, *Altägyptische Tiergeschicte und Fabel*, Darmstadt, 1970, figs. 2 and 18, p. 2, Note 5. This work contains the entire current bibliography on the subject.

Desroches Noblecourt *et alii*
Catalogue of the Ramsès le Grand exhibition, Paris, 1976, No. XXXI, pp. 134-135

The humor of this papyrus fragment is two-faceted. The origin of the object is unknown but it may well have come from the craftsmen's village on the western bank of Thebes.

The animals are shown as derived from human beings, not only in their attitude but also in their dress and manner; in addition, the world, so to speak, is expressed upside-down. The weak is served by the strong, the thief chases the constable. From left to right may be seen a cat rearing up on its hind legs, seemingly offering something to a mouse which is larger than it is. The rodent is treated as a lady of status, dressed in a long transparent robe with fringes which nevertheless allow the tail to hang out. The seat is in the shape of a diabolo of non-Egyptian appearance (a trap?). Under its feet is a stool. The mouse with large, round ears, seemingly adorned with a white loop on which a shell is drawn, wears a voluminous wig evoking Hathor, the patron of love. It holds a goblet, indicating the cat was offered the beverage which it will bring to its lips. Another cat completes the hairdo of the lady. The scene, transposed, is a reminder of that on the sarcophagus of Kawit of the 11th dynasty (Cairo Museum), which, however, had been buried since that time. On it, one sees the princess with a chamberlain who is pouring her something to drink while her chambermaid readjusts a curl of her hair. On the wig of the mouse, the busy cat has a long black curl planted in a tuft of hair in front of one of its ears. The curl holds a large hairpin. ("Draughtsmen's boards" must have existed in the workshops.)

The papyrus has no hieroglyphic texts. If it did, one would undoubtedly find the words the chamberlain says to Lady Kawit: "To your health, O my mistress".

At the rear, a smaller cat advances towards the scene and, in a large white cloth, holds on its lap a little mouse in an astonishingly modern manner. The animal's tail sticks out and an earring (?) may be noted, similar to that of its mother. A larger feline walking towards the mistress, a basket suspended from one of its front paws, holds in front of it a sort of plant screen designed to protect the mouse offspring from the sun.

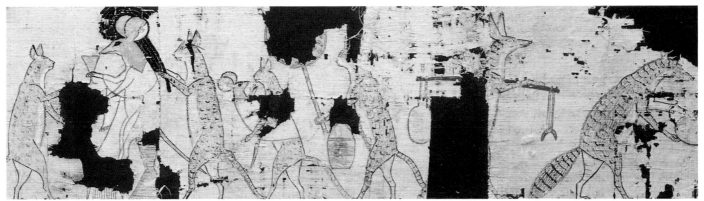

Detail

The sequence stops there. A scene then unfolds in
the opposite direction. Despite deterioration of the
papyrus, it is possible to distinguish a fox carrying two
water jugs on a yoke. The fox has stopped and another
of its species has picked up one jug to pour the contents into a watering-trough still dyed blue. In front of
it, a bovidae lays lazily in an enclosure. The animal
wears a speckled black and ochre-red robe with a
white background. The horns are blue. In the rear,
another fragment gives a glimpse of the vestiges of a
fox headed towards the right.

This papyrus is not unique; other examples show
an orchestra in which hippopotami, donkeys and other
animal species replace beautiful women who stroke
the strings of instruments or blow on double oboes.
They are modelled on the subjects of paintings decorating Theban sanctuaries with graceful lady-musi-
cians. Elsewhere, a citadel is attacked by cats in the
guise of infantrymen or chariot-drivers. Other animal
silhouettes appear in these artists' studies or *ostraca*.
In the lot are included other small drawings where one
finds the illustration of fables reported by Aesop and
repeated by Lafontaine, such as, for example, that of
the wolf and the kid.

Catalogue entry number of the Cairo Museum: 39,867

Dimensions
Height: 0.165 m
Height of the goat: 0.095 m
Diameter of the opening: 0.089

Medium
Gold and silver

Technique
Lip of the vase pad-shaped, covered with a gold leaf turned down on the two sides. Animal-shaped gold handle representing a goat kneeling on a plate of the same metal ending in palmettes attached to the neck through two golden rivets. Back legs soldered to the upper part of the belly of the vessel. Body of the animal made in two sections with perfectly polished joints. The legs, tail, ears and horns are set in. Hammered and engraved decoration.

Condition
Very good. Belly ripped out as the object was being removed. Restored with a plaster casting inside.

Provenance
Bubastis (Zagazig)

Date
19th Dynasty (?): 1320-1200 BC

Bibliography
Edgar, *Engraved Designs on a Silver Vase from Tell Basta*, in *ASAE* XXV (1925), pp. 256-258, Pl. I-II
Vernier, *Bijoux* I, pp. 416-417, No. 53, 262 and II, Pl. CV

Desroches Noblecourt *et alii*
Catalogue of Ramsès le Grand exhibition, Paris, 1976, No. LX, pp. 288-293

This celebrated vessel is one of the jewels of the Cairo Museum. The style and workmanship of the gold and silver object, the shape of the hieroglyphs on the shoulder, the scenes depicted, the small vignette on the belly and, finally, the attitude of the charming goat rearing up on its hind legs, its front legs propped against the top of the neck, the better to sniff with an outstretched muzzle, or to be as close as possible to the liquid the vessel contained, all make it possible to date the object to the Ramses II period and also to determine how much its creator was influenced by the Middle East.

The silver vessel, whose base is engraved with a large white lotus, was found in 1906 with several other gold pieces in two lots buried in the earth near Zagazig, ancient Bubastis, when workers were building a railroad. Consequently, it is often called the "vessel of Zagazig". Undoubtedly, the site was a hiding-place where a thief, perhaps being pursued, buried the stolen booty in a tomb. The complementary presence of two magnificent bracelets of Ramses (cf. 23) helps date the whole.

The inscription appearing on the shoulders of the vessel reveals the prayer addressed to the owner of the object. It reads "May your ka be on you and may you pass millions of years in life and power... For the ka of the royal cupbearer, Temtaneb".

On the belly, a vignette portrays the high royal civil servant in Ramesside ceremonial costume, separated from a goddess he venerates by a libation support adorned with a lotus. The goddess, bearing a great sign of life, brandishes a sceptre crowned with a sort of swallow. The latter element and the strange headdress of the goddess place it in a category still almost unknown. The decoration on the belly is made up of 45 horizontal rows of ova, superimposed in vertical lines. At the ends, the elements are heart-shaped.

The narrower neck is straight and, connecting the two parts of the vessel, a goat—the *gazella-dorcas* of Syria—is shown in an attitude which is as realistic as it is attractive. The theme is found in Mesopotamia, in Elam and in Iran: the animals are erect on either side of a tree in a dance of the mating season.

The neck is decorated with incisions on two parallel sections enveloping the object. The scenes on the lower level refer to life in the Egyptian countryside. A boat is revealed containing a small sanctuary in which a bird lifts a wing. Also on the inside, a bow-net appears to be carried by a basket. There are three large stems of papyrus towards which the boat seems to slide and then one sees a man equipped with a cross-belt, holding one of the papyri in one hand and a duck in the other. He is turned towards a small pond dominated by two other web-footed birds flying above a nest with three large eggs. On the water, another nest with four eggs appears to float not far from a bird which seems to be landing and three swimming fish, including a *tilapia*. A man dressed like the first conveys two *tilapia*, a basket and a bow-net, using a yoke. He is walking towards a larger bouquet of papyrus. Swiftly flying away are the helpless wild ducks which were able to escape the net just stretched onto a larger pond. In it are web-footed birds which are seen to have been captured. A man seizes one duck by the neck in front of a hexagonal net. Two of his comrades pull the cord towards a last bouquet of papyri. This is how harmful animals of the Egyptian marshes were captured.

   The upper section illustrates the progress of an almost mythological hunt in the desert. The hillocks of sand are evoked by centred, dotted circles. This suggests the struggle of animals favorable to man attacking those which are maleficent, interspersed among scenes of fecundity such as the straddling of two *dorcas* gazelles or the momentary triumph of the lion at the throat of an antelope. Five palmettes of the Syrian type—within them, Egyptian flora are recognized—thus separate the sections where first a griffon appears alone, then groups of two animals—the lion conquering the antelope, the cheetah astride the back of a wild bull calf, the griffon biting the lion, the love-making of gazelles and, finally, the cheetah biting the side of a roaring lion.

Sumptuous life in the palace

The only vestiges of the great royal palace whose remaining walls are sufficiently well preserved are those whose ruins were excavated by English archaeologists in the city of the heretic pharaoh, Amenophis IV-Akhenaten. Created by him in Middle Egypt, the city mushroomed within barely a few years on the site now called Tell el-Amarna, along 10 kilometres of the banks of the Nile. It provides the first example of city planning in Antiquity.

The pharaohs of the 18th dynasty established themselves in Thebes where ancient buildings are now covered by the modern urban centres of Karnak and Luxor on the right bank of the Nile. No one really knows where the great home of Pharaoh was situated. There are some indications, however, that that of Queen Hatshepsut was located north of the great pylon of Karnak. On the left bank of Thebes, south of the temple of Medinet Habu, American archaeologists, in the new capital of Amenophis III, uncovered some ruins of royal palaces at Malkata. There, it is known that not only the sovereign and Queen Tiy lived in extraordinary splendor but that the eldest princess, Sitamun, in turn a Great Royal Wife, occupied a luxurious domain. Undoubtedly, even at the beginning of his return from Tell el-Amarna, the young Tutankhamun, crowned in Thebes at about 10 years of age, lived there with his wife, Ankhsenamun.

Starting with the reign of Ramses I, the choice of residence was a different matter. The pharaohs, perhaps to escape the overbearing tutelage of the priests of Amun, wanted to be closer not only to the eastern borders of the country which had to be vigilantly controlled, but also to Memphis where numerous barracks were built under the authority of the princely heir to the crown.

This did not prevent the pharaohs from owning secondary palaces, especially those located in the enclosures of their jubilee temples in various parts of Egypt. The ruins of that of Ramses II were discovered in the first courtyard of the Ramesseum, at the southeastern corner.

It is a matter of record that no place was dearer to the heart of the great pharaoh than the city called Pi-Ramses-Great-of-Victories where his immediate ancestors had already lived and which was subsequently called Pi-Ramses-Great-Ka-of-Horakhty. There, the king glittered like the sun and could worship the great gods and goddesses of the Empire in the majestic temples he had had built. There, more than elsewhere, Seth, the patron of the dynasty, was venerated. The nearby lake witnessed a terrifying naval battle when the Hyksos were chased from ancient Avaris which had risen along its banks. In all the lyrical writings which the new city inspired its poets, it appears the seaport on one of the branches of the Nile ("the Waters of Re"), the great expanses where cavalry could deploy and exercise, the garrisons and the arsenals, could not change the bucolic, luxuriant nature nor the famous façades of residences decorated with glazed turquoise and blue lapis lazuli tiles, still adorned in this way during the reign of Sethos II. Floors and walls were covered with glazed slabs or, sometimes, as under Amenophis III, with paintings made on a plaster surface. The high columns of the halls of state were often dominated by capitals in imitation of palm heads. Garlands of flowers holding flocks of birds capped the shafts. Extreme importance was attached to the apartments of the queen, the favorite Great Royal Wife of the moment, as well as to those of the Great Royal Mother. The quarters of the princes and princesses, who were separated at adolescence, were probably not far from those of the secondary wives and the rooms where numerous concubines lived. There was also the very famous Great Harem on the shores of Lake Karun in the Fayum which housed influential ladies of the palace who were beginning to age. Texts tell us that the royal customs official headed the great royal spinning workshops where the most transparent linens were woven for offering as presents to western sovereigns. Literary libraries complemented recreational locations; even then, dance and music largely constituted one of the most graceful female activities. Such a residence naturally required the services of administrators, majordomos and many servants. On the other hand, it is impossible to rule out the presence of eunuchs assigned to this house of royal ladies.

The furniture of the sovereign and his family was no less sumptuous than that of Tutankhamun. The low beds with animal legs were plated with gold, the chairs and armchairs were encrusted with ivory and glass paste; stools and folding beds were reserved for travelling. The entire court was often required to accompany the king when he journeyed to the great cities and sanctuaries. (From the account of the Battle of Qadesh, it is even known that women and children followed the escort of the sovereign.) Clothing was kept in chests, often carried on stretchers. Pharaoh brought gold or silver dishes with him on his trips. Only the liturgical furniture remained in the temples; the priests kept jealous guard over it.

Floor tiles from a royal palace of Ramses

Catalogue entry numbers of the Cairo Museum: a) 89,479 b) 89,484 c) 89,480 d) 89,483

Dimensions
a)
Length: 0.315 m
Width: 0.159 m
Thickness: 0.027 m
b)
Length: 0.172 m
Max. width: 0.132 m
Thickness: 0.027 m
c)
Length: 0.187 m
Width: 0.135 m
Thickness: 0.027 m
d)
Max. height: 0.189 m
Width: 0.184 m
Thickness: 0.027 m

Medium
Glazed terracotta

Technique
Very "expressionist" drawings, painted before baking

Condition
Fragmentary floor-tiles, three of them broken but restored

Provenance
Qantîr

Date
Probably Ramses II

Bibliography
Hayes, *Glazed Tiles from a Palace of Ramesses II at Kantir*, New York, 1937
Bietak, *Tell el-Dab'a II (Untersuchungen der Zweigstelle Cairo des öesterreichischen Archäologischen Institues, Band I*, Vienna, 1975, p. 23

Desroches Noblecourt *et alii*
Catalogue of Ramsès le Grand exhibition, Paris, 1976, No. LV, (a-d), pp. 277-279

The tiling of some rooms in the royal apartments of Pi-Ramses, in the region of Qantîr, was made of delicate elements of glazed terracotta. The motifs, from end to end, were to represent the fountain of a garden, full of flowers and animals and bordered with the most sought-after graceful plants. The most beautiful women in the world strolled there. All things considered, the tiles were the prefiguration of the Persian carpet. Several museums have been able to acquire examples of the tiles similar to those shown here, undoubtedly from clandestine digs—the statement cannot be proven—which formerly took place in the region.

The fragments exhibited here provide an excellent idea of the elegance of the lines and tones used in decorating royal floors. The rather naturalist style relates these works to those of the Armanian period which may have influenced, more than one may think, the cities of the North, where the technique is believed to have continued some time after the art workshops of the heretic city had been closed.

17
Duck

The web-footed bird swims in a pond, suggested by broken vertical lines, disrupting the blue-green color of the water and by flowers and lotus leaves. The marsh duck is identified by its small pointed wings and the characteristic design of the rump. The range of colors of the purplish-brown plumage is exceedingly delicate, contrasting strongly with the bright, irridescent colors of the classical floral friezes.

The wild duck, which was considered the refuge of the cunning, is found in representations of hunting with boomerangs. Its neck is broken or it is shot through with arrows. Only during the Amarnian period, which rejected all magic, were these winged creatures shown completely free. Through this detail, this decoration again points to the Amarnian influence.

18
Tilapia nilotica or *bulti* of the Nile

This is the *inet* fish of the ancient Egyptians (the chromis), one of the best known in Egypt. Its shape is characteristic. Here, it is completely free. When the artist was unable to play with unreal and original tones like those of Qantîr, he abandoned the purplish and brown colors to classically give this fish the ''resurrection'' (which expresses the hope of Christians, by the play on words *ichtus*) through a bluish body and pink fins. The *inet* is heading towards a large lotus.

19
Mullet

The polychromy on this fragment is slightly brighter.
Blue and green colors are seen. This fish was also frequently found in Egypt and it could measure up to 0.60
m. The mullet represented has an easily recognizable,
V-shaped caudal fin and it is "drawn from life". The
representation of these two completely different fish
illustrates to what extent they were familiar to the riv-
erside dwellers of the Nile.

    A detail should be pointed out: from the Early
Period, the Egyptians used the eggs of the mullet to
make botargo (*beterek*).

20
Woman with hollyhock

The visitor is now introduced to an even more poetic
style. The craftsman portrays a young woman with
black wig, adorned with bracelets and earrings. Her
head is crowned with an especially large lotus flower.
It is difficult to know what she is doing. She stands
before a hollyhock and, holding a small stick, seems to
be thrusting it into one of the blossoms.

    The background of this broken tile, which was
probably rectangular, is blue-green. The fruit appearing in place of the flower once the latter wilted are real-
istically shown in white.

Like the poppy and the blueberry, the hollyhock was imported from Syria during the New Kingdom. This tile may have covered a wall, probably in the throne room, judging from the arrangement of the decoration. This interpretation should raise no objection since English archaeologists, in the ruins of the palace of Tell el-Amarna, discovered mural coverings where half-tones were the rule—light green, white, light blue, golden yellow, purple and some touches of black suggesting elegant graminaceous flowers surrounded by their leaves, on a background strewn with white and yellow daisies in relief.

Provisional catalogue entry number of the Cairo Museum: a) 5-2-24-7
Catalogue entry number of the Cairo Museum: b) 33,968

Dimensions
a)
Length: 0.231 m
Width: 0.11 m
Thickness: 0.02 m
b)
Length: 0.078 m
Width: 0.12 m
Thickness: 0.02 m

Medium
Enamelled frit, opaque glass paste

Technique
Molded and inlaid with colored paste

Condition
a) Complete briquette broken and restored
b) Fragment

Provenance
Western Thebes, Temple of Medinet Habu

Date
Ramses III

Bibliography
Maspero, *Guide*, p. 501, No. 5125
Daressy, *Plaquettes émaillées de Médinet-Habou* in *ASAE* XI (1910),
    pp. 49 and ff.

Desroches Noblecourt *et alii*
Catalogue of the Ramsès le Grand exhibition, Paris, 1976,
    No. LVII (a-b), pp. 280-281

These hybrid birds with characteristic crest, wings lifted in the rear, a broad horizontal tail and long legs outstretched in front are plovers with triangular claws, shown by the Egyptians since the very Early Period. They were quickly provided with arms in an attitude of veneration. In this way, the Egyptians, by giving them an anthropomorphic element, sought to rank them in a slightly lower human category. The star often shown under the lifted arm, used in this case to write the word "worship", indicates that these people, thus symbolized and gradually associated with Egypt, worshipped Pharaoh. No one doubts they had been conquered; their wings, folded backwards, seem to impede their flight. They are seen in numerous official scenes. Sometimes, they are even held in the hand of a young person. Here, they are placed on a straw basket, woven in a checker-board design in mauve, dark blue and blue-green. The star visible in the series of birds which succeed one another is white. A constant element, appearing under the very round eye, is a very long canthus.

These fragments of enamelled terracotta come from the temple "of millions of years" of Ramses III at Medinet Habu and thus date to the 20th dynasty. But the motifs were probably virtually the same on some monuments of Ramses II. The glazed terracotta is rather discreet in its coloring. In the same style is the image of foreign peoples in Egypt, modelled in small figurines evoking the different ethnic origins known by the Egyptians–the Sudanese, with the ornamented leather loincloth, the Babylonian with the long multi-colored robe, the Libyan with the lock of hair, etc.

In several Ramesside temples, these *rekhyt* appear as kneeling men. They are readily recognized by the high curved crest of the plover on their skulls.

22

Articulated floral frieze

Catalogue entry number of the Cairo Museum: 21,842

Dimensions
Max. height: 0.077 m
Length: 0.60 m

Medium
Enamelled frit, colored pastes

Technique
Molded elements assembled in a frieze. Inlaid colored pastes

Condition
Elements broken and restored in 1975-76

Provenance
Delta: Shibin el-Kôm in the Minufiya

Date
Ramses III (1198-1166 BC)

Bibliography
Maspero, *Guide*, p. 500, No. 5115
Hayes, *Scepter* II, p. 368, Fig. 232

Desroches Noblecourt *et alii*
Catalogue of Ramsès le Grand exhibition, Paris, 1976,
    No. LVIII, p. 282

Likely also dating to the reign of Ramses III, these vestiges of an articulated floral frieze made of glazed overlapping terracotta were intended to suggest garlands of fresh flowers displayed on festival days at the top of walls and columns, on the backs of seats and even on the chests of guests.

Several museums have examples, all of which seem to date to the early 20th dynasty. With the enamelled frit are mixed colored pastes of purer, brighter tones. Here, one again finds the polychromy which covered all the reliefs of the temples with glowing colors and no half-tones. These elements come from the Delta and probably adorned a royal domain. The white motifs, the turquoise blues, the browns, the yellow, green, lapis blue and red are set off, inlaid in a gilded limestone background. One recognizes daisies, magnificent Egyptian lotuses with graduated petals which gave to the West their name of nenuphar, poppies and bunches of grapes whose seed shape is still seen.

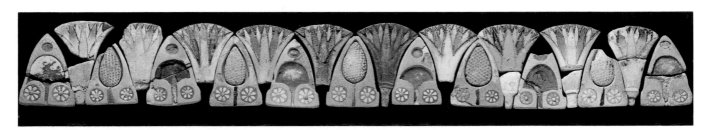

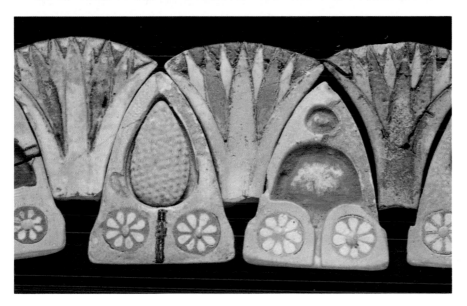

23

Ramses' bracelets

Catalogue entry number of the Cairo Museum: 39,873
General Cairo catalogue: 52,575 and 52,576

Dimensions
Height: 0.06 m
Max. diameter: 0.065 and 0.07 m

Medium
Gold and lapis lazuli

Condition
Slightly deformed

Technique
Granulated work. Birds' heads and tails set in. Hinges include one for closing with a mobile key.

Provenance
Bubastis (Zagazig) treasure discovered in 1906

Date
Ramses II

Bibliography
Porter-Moss IV (1934), pp. 34-35
Vernier, *Bijoux et orfèvreries*, Catalogue général . . . du Musée du Caire (Cairo, 1907-27), No. 52,575 - 52,576
Wilimkova, *Chefs-d'oeuvre de l'art égyptien* (Prague, 1969), No. 69, p. 54
Wilkinson, *Ancient Egyptian Jewellery* (London, 1971), p. 151, Pl. LVII
Aldred, *Jewels of the Pharaohs* (London, 1971), p. 12, Pl. 129

Desroches Noblecourt *et alii*
Catalogue of Ramsès le Grand exhibition, Paris, 1976

Apart from the vessel with the goat-shaped handle, two objects, unquestionably exceptional, were provided by the double treasure of Zagazig, in the form of two magnificent bracelets. The name of the Lord of the Two Lands, Usimaare-Setepenre, the coronation name of Ramses II, is on them. They are unique.

Their worksmanship is a perfect illustration of the beautiful jewelry made at the time of the great king—full shapes with gold and the noble color of lapis lazuli blended. The granulated technique is used lavishly.

The two jewels are hinged in order that they may be easily slipped over the wrist. The upper part, obviously the most ornamented, is the widest. The central element is made of a single piece of lapis lazuli from which emerge two heads of wild ducks, curved backwards. A large, flared gold tail roughly imitates long feathers. The intermediate part between the convex body and the tail consists of two granulated decorative areas with diamond shapes and small rosettes. The two ducks are flanked by two triangular granulated areas which, between them, form a flat, undulated ribbon. Around and fanning outwards, a border of pearly, ringed or V-shaped elements is shown near the rear hinges. In the clasp section, fine granulated areas recall the ornamentation which separated the tail and breast of the animals. The most carefully finished motif is obviously that of the birds' heads. The natural areas of colored feathers are marked by veins in relief.

The object is truly royal and worthy of Ramses. He wears an example adorned with a voluminous eye, the *wdjat*, on a bust exhibited here (cf. *in fine*, 67). Other bracelets from the New Kingdom are known—among the jewels of Tutankhamun, for example—in which a full scarab of lapis lazuli replaces the ducks. When it comes to female jewelry, the animal motif is less massive. Small prone cats with rearing heads and small, extended hippopotami, etc. appear.

This pair of bracelets is all the more interesting because Ramses' tomb was completely looted in Antiquity. The presence in the Musée du Louvre of some jewelry relics bearing Ramses' name is due to a discovery by August Mariette in the Serapeum of Memphis. The famous Horse Ring, also in the Louvre, was a gift of Mohamed Ali to Charles X. The subject may undoubtedly be interpreted as the tribute by Ramses to the horses which saved him during the celebrated Battle of Qadesh (cf. Preface and last exhibition area).

The existence of the two bracelets in the treasures of Zagazig reconfirms the date of the majority of objects found there. In all probability, he who was rewarded with a gold drinking cup bearing the name of Queen Tewosret was buried with a "family treasure" and no doubt his father, before him, had received gold bracelets from Ramses bearing the name of the great king. Similarly, the man's tomb may have been looted by someone who was then forced to bury his plunder in an attempt to avoid arrest. But this is only a hypothesis and all the necessary reservations apply.

Whatever the case, it is easy to imagine Ramses as he wished to be shown on some of his stelae, posing next to one of his colossi, handing out gold rewards to General Mose and the officers and soldiers of his garrison and, finally, removing from his wrists these magnificent ornaments to give them to one of the bravest artisans of his victories.

As with all jewelry, the bracelets, which probably encircled his wrists, must have played a dual role—decorative as well as protective. We have already alluded several times to the marsh ducks symbolizing pernicious elements which had to be pierced with arrows or whose necks had to be wrung in order that their harmfulness might be eliminated. Here, the twisted necks bear witness to the birds' neutralization; the latter is also evident in their use as furniture legs or even as make-up vessels. Care must be taken not to confuse the marsh ducks with twisted necks and the goose's offspring, the goslings, which symbolize the young royal toddlers. The Louvre possesses the small gosling ring worn by the future Ramses IV when he was a child.

24

Earrings with the names of Sethos II

Catalogue entry number of the Cairo Museum: 39,675
General Cairo catalogue: 52,397 and 52,398

Dimensions
Total height: 0.135 m
Length of the ear ornament: 0.05 m
Width of the trapezium: 0.038 and 0.039 m

Medium
Gold

Technique
Soldered gold sheets (for the blueberries) and articulated middle part. Nested tubes. Fastening scores.

Provenance
Western Thebes; Valley of the Kings; *cachette* of objects bearing the names of Sethos II and Tewosret, his wife. Davis digs, 1908

Date
Sethos II: *circa* 1210 BC

Bibliography
Porter-Moss, I-2, p. 567
Davis, *The Tomb of Siphtah*, pp. 35-36, Pl. VIII-IX
Vernier, *Bijoux et Orfèvreries*, Catalogue général . . . du Musée du Caire, pp. 137-138, Pl. XXVIII
Aldred, *Jewels of the Pharaohs*, No. 130
Wilkinson, *Ancient Egyptian Jewellery*, p. 155, PL. LX A

Desroches Noblecourt *et alii*
Catalogue of the Ramsès le Grand exhibition, Paris, 1976, No. LXVI (a-b), pp. 302-303

It has been recalled (cf. the sarcophagus of the king's merchant, Piay, 36) that earrings were introduced into Egypt during the New Kingdom under the influence of the Near East. To date, however, there is no known representation of the adult pharaoh with this ornament. On the other hand, some statues of sovereigns, especially those of Ramses and even of some of his subjects, have earlobes which show the mark of a very large opening, suggesting such jewelry was worn. This is undoubtedly an indication designed to recall that the royal personage was thus once adorned.

Here we have magnificent earrings in three sections, all executed in thin gold sheets. First is a horizontal tube which had to be threaded in the ear, ending on one side in a sort of convex button bearing the last and first name of Sethos II, and, on the other, in a flower with its corolla in full bloom, made of eight gadroons culminating in a small central heart. Four cartouches of Sethos II are also inlaid on the flower. The middle part of the piece is composed of two gold sheets soldered in the shape of a trapezium and suspended from the two ends of the fastening tube by two rings on either side of a notch for the earlobe. Two other cartouches of Sethos adorn this element. Finally, at the base are fastened two small rings in which a rod was introduced. On the rod, at intervals, are suspended thin, scored tubes, four of which end in stylized blueberry heads and three others, in similar but much larger elements.

Archaeologists who have experienced the rare emotion of discovering a royal treasure–those of Ahmose and of Tutankhamun–recognized drop earrings among the jewels. We are now convinced these elements either belonged to the child king or were made for funerary trappings in order to foster the rebirth of the deceased in the other world and enable him to enjoy eternal youth. The drop earrings of Tutankhamun also included a sumptuous pair whose top is adorned with a small gosling with a completely transparent blue glass head dominated by its two wings drawn up in the arc of a circle.

The wearing of these earrings by small boys may well have influenced Nubian fashion. Thus, in the parade of the children of chiefs brought back to the court of Tutankhamun by the viceroy of Nubia are young princes, their faces framed with magnificent drop earrings.

25

Ewer of the Pharaoh Ahmose

Catalogue entry number of the Cairo Museum: 85,895

Dimensions
Height: 0.146 m
Max. diameter (belly): 0.05 m
Diameter of the base: 0.04 m
Diameter of the opening (spout): 0.017 m

Medium
Gold

Technique
Object made of four soldered parts

Condition
Excellent

Provenance
Tanis, tomb of Psusennes

Date
Early 18th dynasty

Bibliography
Montet, *Psousennès*, p. 97; No. 393, Pl. LXV
Helck, *Nilhöhe und Jubiläumsfest, ZÄS* 93, 1966, p. 74
Schott, *Die heilige Vase des Amun, ZÄS* 98, 1970, p. 42 and ff.
Traunecker, *Les rites de l'eau à Karnak, BIFAO* 72 (1972),
    pp. 203 and ff.

Desroches Noblecourt *et alii*
Catalogue of the Ramsès le Grand exhibition, Paris, 1976,
    No. LXI, pp. 294-295

Like other elements of gold and silver tableware, this precious object was found in the tomb of Psusennes, a pharaoh of the 21st dynasty who was buried late in the 11th century BC at Tanis, in the Delta, where the court had been established. It was certainly because the treasures of the temples of the ancient capital of Pi-Ramses were partially brought to Tanis that this vessel along with other gold pieces from the site were discovered in the necropolis of the new dynasty.

The residence of the Ramessides probably had been set up on the ancient site of Avaris where the liberator of Egypt, Ahmose, drove out the Hyksos occupiers.

For several reasons, therefore, this ewer is particularly worthy of interest. One must admire the pure lines which are so significant in an Egyptian vessel and the sobriety of its decoration. Dominated by the sign of the sky, the ewer bears, on two vertical columns, the following inscription: "the living god (or god incarnate) Nebpehtyre (Ahmose's coronation name), justified, beloved of Osiris, Lord of Abydos".

The object is made of several parts which are soldered together—the flared foot, the slender belly, the spout, the neck and its nesting rim. Scenes in which Pharaoh holds this libation utensil by the most tapered part of the foot are frequent. The beneficiary of the rite is obviously the divinity. In writings, this type of accessory is called the *senebet*. It was also supposed to contain a sample of the flood water. A text from the temple of Karnak, dating to Tuthmosis III, comments on this type of vessel as being "similar to the stars under the abdomen of the goddess Nut".

26

Drinking vessel of Queen Tewosret

Catalogue entry number of the Cairo Museum: 39,872
General Cairo catalogue: 53,260

Dimensions
Total height: 0.095
Height of the foot: 0.04
Diameter of the cup: 0.08 m
Diameter of the base: 0.043 m

Medium
Gold

Technique
Poorly worked

Provenance
Bubastis (Zagazig)

Date
Queen Tewosret

Bibliography
Porter-Moss IV, p. 35
Edgar in Maspero, *Le Musée Egyptien* II, p. 99, Pl. XLIV (1)
Vernier, *Bijoux et Orfèvreries*, Catalogue général . . . du Musée du
     Caire, p. 415, Pl. CIV

On the lotus:
Keimer, *Revue de l'Égypte ancienne* II, pp. 232-253
Chalice of Tutankhamun: *Toutankhamon et son temps*,
     Paris, 1967, No. 42

Desroches Noblecourt *et alii*
Catalogue of the Ramsès le Grand exhibition, Paris, 1976,
     No. LXII, pp. 296-297

The visitor now returns to the atmosphere of the treasure of Zagazig where the famous vessel with the goat-shaped handle was found. The least one may say is that if this treasure were composed of objects belonging to the owner of this exceptional piece–the royal cup-bearer, Temtaneb–he must have lived at least until the end of the 19th dynasty in order to possess a cup bearing the name of a successor of Sethos II–Queen Tewosret, who mounted the throne of Egypt for a few years between 1204 and 1196.

The workmanship of the magnificent vessels exhibited illustrates the care goldsmiths and engravers took. However, the technique was undoubtedly slightly impoverished by the end of the dynasty. The chalice, made of two parts soldered together with an alloy including verdigris, consisted of a foot flared in a corolla at the base, marked with small leaflets emerging from a triple bond and from the vessel itself, espousing the shape of a large lotus with four sepals and 12 petals in inlaid relief.

The gold sheet is extremely thin and has been subjected to some impact and to deterioration. Mainly in Tell el-Amarna, on reliefs of high civil servants in the civilian necropolis, are scenes in which members of the royal family drink from similar cups which they hold not by the foot, but by the belly, as if to bring wine to room temperature.

Here, the two species of Egyptian lotus are suggested–not the blue lotus with pointed petals, but the white lotus, which is more voluminous and has round-edged petals. Nevertheless, this is a species of hybrid in which the elements of the *seshen*–the blue lotus from which the name Suzanne derives and the white lotus, *nefer*: (ne) nuphar–are apparently combined.

27

Zagazig necklace

Catalogue entry number of the Cairo Museum: 39,875
General Cairo catalogue: 53,184

Dimensions
Max. width of the present mounting: 0.36 m

Medium
Gold or gold alloy (traces of grey-black oxide on some elements)
    and cornelian

Technique
Artificial mounting of the elements; clasps missing

Condition
The mounting is modern.

Provenance
Bubastis (Zagazig)

Date
19th dynasty (?)

Bibliography
Edgar in Maspero, *Le Musée Égyptien* II, pp. 104-105, Pl. LII
Vernier, *Bijoux et Orfèvreries*, Catalogue général . . . du Musée du
    Caire, p. 388, Pl. LXXXIII
Wilkinson, *Ancient Egyptian Jewellery*, p. 152, Pl. LVIII B

Desroches Noblecourt *et alii*
Catalogue of the Ramsès le Grand exhibition, Paris, 1976

Scattered among one of the two Zagazig treasures were numerous small cornelian, gold and probably electrum pearls, allowing this throat-piece to be reassembled. The mounting is artificial but should generally correspond to reality. However, this type of necklace was often complemented by two solid motifs in the form of lotus flowers, linking the various rows of pearls with the clasp. Some suggest stylized blueberries. The gold elements are suspended from a small ring while those of cornelian are merely pierced. Most of this neck jewelry, called "wide necklaces" (*wesekh*), is made of precious metal and semi-precious stones or of small, colored, glazed terracotta motifs imitating the magnificent collars of natural flowers worn by ladies and even men on festival days and by guests at funerary banquets.

The style of the elements making up this jewel is completely in keeping with those of Ramesside necklaces (cf. the bust of Meryetamun, 28).

28

Eldest daughter of Ramses and Nefertari

Catalogue entry number of the Cairo Museum: 31,413
General Cairo catalogue: 600

Dimensions
Height: 0.75 m
Width: 0.44 m
Depth: 0.44 m

Medium
Painted limestone

Technique
Refined where the velvet-like quality of the limestone has been fully
    exploited

Condition
Broken at the waist

Provenance
Western Thebes, sanctuary of the "white queen", northwest of the
    Ramesseum. Discovered in 1896

Date
Ramses II

Summary bibliography
Petrie, *Six Temples* I (London, 1897), pp. 6-7, 22, Pl. XXIII
Borchardt, *Statuen*, II, p. 152, No. 600
Vandier, *Manuel*, III, pp. 427-428
Nims-Swaan, *Thebes of the Pharaohs* (London, 1965), p. 134
Wenig, *Die Frau im alten Ägypten* (Leipzig, 1967), Pl. 76
Porter-Moss, II (Oxford, 1972), p. 431
Susuki, *Sculptures of the World*, 3, Egypt
    (Shogakukan, 1975), Pl. 76
Almagro, *Arte faraonico* (Madrid-Barcelona, 1975)

Desroches Noblecourt *et alii*
Catalogue of the Ramsès le Grand exhibition, Paris, 1976,
    No. XIV, pp. 72-74

For the name of the queen:
Yahyà Salàh Sabr Al-Masri, *Excavations in Akhmin*,
    in *ASAE* LXIX, Cairo, 1983, pp. 4-13, Pl. I-IX

For many years, this fragment of a statue sculpted in an extremely fine limestone which still bears traces of color and even a few touches of gold remained anonymous. Found in 1896 in a sanctuary northwest of the Ramesseum by F.L. Petrie, it had commonly been called "the queen with the *menat* or the "white queen" because the white of her robe is still virtually immaculate and her skin light. The face thus stands out, surrounded by the voluminous curled headdress with traces of lapis lazuli blue.

Fate, however, smiles upon the Egyptologist who is willing to be patient. The princess was identified through the fortuitous discovery October 17, 1981 of vestiges of a colossal statue of the Great Royal Wife and the Royal Daughter Meryetamun about 4.5 m below ground level as a construction crew built the foundations of a future administrative complex at Akhmin, in Upper Egypt.

To make comparison easier, it is appropriate to describe the Ramesseum statue. It consists of the upper body of a young, slender woman with a high bosom. At the small waist starts the swelling of the hips where a break occurred. The preserved left arm of the figure is softly plump through the transparent fabric of the sleeve and the hand folded below the right breast bears an insignia which is seen held by women performing a religious act—it is the *menat*, a sort of elongated, truncated palette dominated here by a woman's head and ending in a rosette evoking the uterus. In the rear, a sort of pad appears, made of pearls and serving as a necklace, suggesting hair rising out of the skull. Often, in the other hand, the officiant holds a sistrum—a musical instrument with a series of small castanets which crackle when the bronze object is shaken.

These two ritual elements are assigned only to women. They used them, before the sovereign, to evoke the god or the deceased, the first blush of love, the announcement of a birth, modeled on that of the solar child. Queens above all often had these insignia which emphasized one of their essential roles in regard to the creative principle as well as to its representative on earth, Pharaoh.

Meryetamun appears to wear a skin-tight robe without pleats. Two rosettes adorn the tunic at chest height. A wide necklace with five rows of *nefer* hieroglyphs, suggesting "beauty" and, at the same time, "youth", ends in pendants in the shape of drops. It is a genuine collar covering the top of the shoulders and setting off the neck, which has two small wrinkles, a detail which appeared starting in the Amarnian period. A flat headband covers the upper part of the royal forehead, half hidden by the beginning of an architectural wig of regular, graduated curls, including two flaps limited by a ribbon framing the face and neck and stopping above the chest. The originality of this headdress consists in the fact that it flares out from the forehead to the top of the skull. A double headband crosses it and it is adorned in the centre with two serpent bodies. One serpent's head is dominated by the white crown of Upper Egypt, the other, by the red crown of Lower Egypt. At the top of the wig, a *modius* is bordered by a series of erect, disked serpents. The face of the woman is one of extreme sensitivity and it is influenced by the lighting. The eyes still have color, surrounded by lines of make-up. The upper and lower eyelids come together near the temples, as in a triangle. The brow ridges are almost straight. The shape of the nose, unfortunately broken, mars the harmony of the face, but scrutiny of the mouth brings the viewer back to the incomparable quality of the rather thick lips, the corners turned up in a smile, the lower lip slightly drooping. The small, square chin could be Queen Tuya's own. The high ears, set off by locks of hair, are embellished with two wide, disk-shaped curls.

The type of this statue as well as the much more explicit inscriptions engraved on the back may now be compared with the colossus more than seven m high excavated in 1981 at Akhmin. In the inscriptions, we are told that she is the Superior of the Harem of Amun Re, player of the sistrum of Mut and the player of the *menat* of Hathor. In addition, the Akhmin statue bears the name of the princess—the eldest daughter of the king and Nefertari, Meryetamun—"with the splendid face, magnificent in the palace, the beloved of the Lord of the Two Lands, she who stands by her master like Sothis is beside Orion; one is satisfied with what is said when she opens her mouth to soothe the Lord of the Two Lands" . . . She even holds the majority of the titles which had been assigned to her mother. Well before the death of his beloved wife, Ramses contracted a marriage with the eldest of his daughters, Bintanath, brought into the world for him by his other Great Royal Wife, Istnofret, who is never shown on monuments from the early reign. It would appear that on the death of Nefertari, in the lapse of time until king married the first Hittite princess, he wed Meryetamun,

the beautiful one who in many ways recalled the beloved deceased wife and who became the new Great Royal Wife of Ramses.

29

Support and cuppel usurped (?) by the Pharaoh Psusennes

Catalogue entry number of the Cairo Museum: 86,899

Dimensions
Support
Height: 0.595 m
Diameter: 0.085 m
Cuppel
Depth of the cavity: 0.08 m
Diameter: 0.257 m

Medium
Silver

Technique
Made in one piece (pressed)

Condition
Good

Provenance
Tanis, tomb of Psusennes

Date
Psusennes (1054-1004 BC)

Bibliography
Montet, *Psousennès*, p. 96, No. 391-392, Pl. LXV
Sacred and secular vessels in the tomb of Psusennes,
     Monuments Piot 38 (1941), pp. 17-39,
     Tanis, 1942, pp. 166-168

Desroches Noblecourt *et alii*
Catalogue of the Ramsès le Grand exhibition, Paris, 1976,
     No. LVXIII, pp. 304-305

Found in Psusennes' tomb, this is a sort of basin, hollow in the centre and highly flared at the edge, suggesting, in profile, the appearance of a cuppel. Made of silver and marked with the king's name, it was as if imbedded in an elegant, very slender support with a large foot made of a thick sheet of silver. On the full height of the support is engraved an inscription on a column with the names and protocol of Psusennes. It, states: ''beloved of Osiris and beloved of Ptah-Sokar'' possibly emphasizing the funerary use assigned to the objects.

However, it is probable they date to the reign of Ramses since they were collected during the 21st dynasty among the treasures of the temples of Pi-Ramses (Qantîr-Avaris). For this ritual material, the same origin is assumed as for the ewer of Ahmose. Moreover, the silver support was found near the sarcophagus, placed on a quadrangular bronze base bearing the cartouche of Ramses II.

These silver pieces are in keeping with the long list of cult objects. The walls of the New Kingdom temples provided numerous examples of their execution as well as their use. Suffice it to refer to the door of Sennudjem's tomb (cf. 45) to find a similar support before the divine images of Ptah-Sokar and of Osiris. On it stands a ritual vessel. Again, on the outside panels of the *naos* of the sun sanctuary of Abu Simbel (cf. 2), one recognizes the same supports with a ewer. Elsewhere, the king pours a libation on the cuppel or lights the fire under winged creatures in order to sanctify a holocaust to a faraway divinity.

Catalogue entry number of the Cairo Museum: 85,892

Dimensions
Height: 0.38 m
Max. diameter: 0.089 m

Medium
Gold

Technique
Made in one piece

Condition
Excellent

Provenance
Tanis, tomb of Psusennes

Date
Psusennes (1054-1004 BC)

Bibliography
Montet, *Psousennès*, Pl. LXVII-LXVIII, pp. 99-100, No. 396-397
Vases sacrés et profanes du tombeau de Psousennès,
      Monuments Piot, XXXVIII (1941), pp. 17-39,
      Tanis, (1942), pp. 166-168

Desroches Noblecourt *et alii*
Catalogue of the Ramsès le Grand exhibition, Paris, 1976,
      No. LXIX and No. LXX, pp. 308-309

The bottle is another precious object found in Psusennes' tomb at Tanis. The handle of the bottle is hammered like that of a libation jug without its spout. The
high, slightly curved neck ends in a semi-flared papyrus umbel. Its rim features a rather thick, flat lip. A lig-
ature at the base of the floral head of the leaflets, in
slightly inlaid relief, completes the only plant details
suggested by this flat-bottomed vessel. At shoulder
height, one may see the names and surname of Psusennes dominated by the titles differentiating the birth
and coronation names.

The gold spout, made in a single piece, as well as
the following object–the basin found next to it–are two
elements of an ensemble which appears on the walls
of tombs and temples, often carried by the king's cup-
bearers. Of less precious metal, they were also used
for the lords. It is likely the objects served to wash the
hands after a ceremony or civil meal.

Basin bearing the name of Psusennes

Catalogue entry number of the Cairo Museum: 85,893

Dimensions
Height: 0.17 m
Diameter: 0.102 m

Medium
Gold

Technique
Made in one piece except for the handle, which is attached with
    three rivets

Condition
Excellent

Provenance
Tanis, tomb of Psusennes

Date
Psusennes (1054-1004 BC)

Bibliography
Montet, *Psousennès*, Pl. LXVII-LXVIII, pp. 99-100, No. 396-397
Vases sacrés et profanes du tombeau de Psousennès,
    Monuments Piot, XXXVIII (1941), pp. 17-39,
    Tanis, (1942), pp. 166-168

Desroches Noblecourt *et alii*
Catalogue of the Ramsès le Grand exhibition, Paris, 1976,
    No. LXIX and No. LXX, pp. 308-309

A complement to the bottle which has just been
discussed, with elegant curved line and flared upper
lip, it, too, is made of a thick sheet of gold. A perforated handle attached with three rivets features a lotus
bouquet and ligatured buds. Under the flower, the
stems form the horizontal handle which ends in a
palm-leaf which, like the flower itself, is also attached.
The basin as well is marked with the name of Psusennes.

In the Old Kingdom, the object was rather heavy in
form. Subsequently, it was given a more elegant profile. The bottle with the long spout from the Old Kingdom which it accompanied was transformed into a
slender flask with a spout, easier to carry in the arms
of the cup-bearers than a pot-bellied object, and more
so because the lustration water it contained made it
heavier.

The visitor is again in the presence of eating utensils, be they divine, funerary or civilian, whose evolved
style appeared in tombs and temples early in the New
Kingdom. When one considers Egypt's degeneration
during the 21st dynasty, it is easy to imagine why Psusennes usurped one of the sanctuaries of Ramses'
capital for the benefit of his funerary furnishings.

Necklace bearing the name of Psusennes

Catalogue entry number of the Cairo Museum: 85,571

Dimensions
Total height: 0.645 m
Max. int. diameter: 0.135 m
Total height of the small chains (flowers included): 0.307 m
Height of the counterweight clasp: 0.109
Width of the counterweight clasp: 0.073 m
Thickness of the counterweight clasp: 0.02 m

Medium
Gold and lapis lazuli

Technique
Threaded gold rings; "column" chains of various sizes; inlaid clasp

Condition
Quite good; some parts and inlays missing

Provenance
Tanis, tomb of Psusennes

Date
21st dynasty (1054-1004 BC)

Bibliography
Montet, *Psousennès*, II, pp. 136-137, No. 483, Pl. CVIII
Montet, *Colliers royaux trouvés dans les tombes de Tanis* in
        *Fondation E. Piot, Monuments et Mémoires des Inscriptions
        et Belles-Lettres*, V. XLI (1946), pp. 5-22, Pl. II, Fig. 4

Desroches Noblecourt *et alii*
Catalogue of the Ramsès le Grand exhibition, Paris, 1976,
        No. LXVIII, pp. 306-307

Found by Pierre Montet at Tanis in the same funerary treasure of Psusennes, this sumptuous necklace is made of small threaded gold coins, a trapezoidal-shaped clasp and a cluster of flowers attached to small chains forming counterweights. It is veritable golden fleece.

The main part of the throat-piece consisted of six rows; only five were found. The present mounting of the piece weighs some 8,640 grams. The rings were slipped on wads of threads in very dense skeins attached to the clasp. The latter, like a case, had six holes on each side to thread the small golden coins. At the top, a winged scarab pushes the sun. Then, shown on the two cartouches of Psusennes flanking a small papyrus column, are traces of blue inlays which are still visible. At the top and at the base of this large motif, one may admire two friezes of disked cobras engraved on a lapis lazuli background. Fourteen column chains are fastened to the clasp, ending in a bindweed. From each bindweed are suspended two thinner columns, each in turn ending in a bindweed from which hang two even thinner column chains, each ending in a new bindweed. The whole is made up of a row of 14 small bells, then 28, ending in 56 pendants.

The pharaohs often were represented wearing large necklaces on their chests but this necklace must have been even more cumbersome—in fact, of unbearable weight—during long ceremonies. The second king of the 21st dynasty may again have had looted a sanctuary built by Ramses containing one of the sacred barques. The necklace, as was often the case, undoubtedly completed the ornaments of the figure-head. Examples are visible on the bas-reliefs of temples.

Detail of exhibit 66

Detail of exhibit 4

Daily life of craftsmen of the royal necropolis and preparation for immortality

At Deir el-Medina, digs carried out for almost 50 years by the École Française d'Archéologie Orientale of Cairo, under the direction of Bernard Bruyère, produced unique documents thanks to excavation of the village and necropolis of the craftsmen of royal tombs, covered by thousands of tons of rubbish. It is an exceptional complex where several generations succeeded one another–families of quarrymen and artists and sculptors who lived in a village specially designed for this purpose in the 18th dynasty. However, the village assumed its full significance during the following reigns. The craftsmen were called the "Servants of the Place of Truth" and members of the Team of the Tomb (*Pa Kher*), thereby recalling their essential responsibility–to dig and decorate the tombs of the kings and queens. Enjoying a special status, they were placed under the authority of the vizier but were obviously led by intermediate superintendents who divided them into two groups–the right and left groups, each headed by a foreman with an assistant. Administrative responsibilities were entrusted to a scribe who handled accounting and who reported directly to the vizier.

Like all Egyptians of the time, the craftsmen had one day off every ten days and were relieved of certain duties by auxiliary staff–unskilled workmen, fishermen, hunters, peasants and civil servants of the royal granaries who supplied them with food. There were also guards to watch over tombs under construction. Once the tombs were finished, the sealed entrances were regularly monitored by a surveillance team until Pharaoh's death. The team, naturally, was strengthened by guards and inspections. The village where these men and their families lived was made up of houses with at least three main rooms and a porch. The houses were symmetrically distributed on each side of a central street–an arrangement corresponding to the "port" and "starboard" sides of the group. Situated within a surrounding wall, the village was guarded by its own police force, the *medjay*, whose station was located in the north, near a source of water and some major houses on the square. Not only did these craftsmen leave us magnificent mural illustrations in their tombs, often worthy of the drawing quality found in the royal hypogea, but also precious evidence of daily life, thanks to the funerary furniture of tombs which had not been looted. Moreover, documents abandoned by foremen, superintendents and scribes, found on papyrus and *ostraca* in the ruins, have enabled philologists, mainly Dr. J. Černý, to reconstitute the quality and pace of their activity, a portion of the school *curricula*, the craftsmen's daily concerns, their corporative and family life, their loves, quarrels, disputes and even trials. The facts are a far cry from the fables of the first Greek travellers who claimed that once the tomb of the king was completed, the workers who had built it were put to death! The existence of these families may thus be followed for several generations. All left their village to go down into the royal valleys, those where the sovereigns were buried during three dynasties (the Valley of the Kings); the Valley of the West, where before and after the Amarnian heresy, Amenophis III and Ay were interred; where the silex tools still used to dig the tombs were resharpened. The Valley of the Queens was also familiar to them. The mummies of the Great Royal Wives and of some princes had been placed there since the 19th dynasty. They also knew another valley, south of the Valley of the Queens, called Wadi Taget Zeid where Queen Hatshepsut had her first tomb built when she was only a Great Royal Wife. Not far away, Tuthmosis III dedicated a common tomb for his three secondary Syrian wives.

The craftsmen walked along roads which led them to their work. Often, especially during hot weather, they stopped at the Pass of the Valley, dominated by the great natural pyramid of Thebes where vestiges of their provisional camps have been found. Nearby, they had built tiny chapels with dry stones, dedicated to the Goddess-who-lives-at-the-Summit and to the god Amun. Traces of their passage still exist. Along the entire rocky piedmont, the mountain of Thebes bears the mark of long white trails, evidence of their travels. Sometimes, one sees a staircase built into the rock by the craftsmen. Elsewhere, sheltered by immense boulders, are shaded sites perfect for naps before they resumed work. The craftsmen left graffiti on the walls, commenting on their choices or addressing a prayer to the Sacred-summit-which-strikes-evil-ones-with-blindness. When, as throughout the desert, rains fell, torrential as they were ephemeral, an inscription celebrates this "water from the sky" which almost formed a lake in the hollows of the rock. The family is then invited to admire the miracle!

The entire existence of this so typically Egyptian population was restored to life with exceptional intensity. Even today, it is evoked by objects found in craftsmen's tombs, mainly those of the famous Sennudjem, whose tomb as well as the vestiges of his house are among the most important relics of Deir el-Medina. In contemplating the wall decorations and funerary trappings of the tomb he shared with several generations of his family, we are convinced his descendants built the "Houses of Eternity" of Sethos I, of Ramses II, of the queens and Great Royal Wives, along with those of the princes and princesses around them.

33

● Evocation of some figures
Cover of the outer sarcophagus
of Sennudjem

Catalogue entry number of the Cairo Museum: 27,308

Dimensions
Height: 1.845 m
Max. width (elbows): 0.50 m
Depth (feet): 0.31 m

Medium
Stuccoed and painted wood; varnished

Technique
Face, feet, hands and beard set in: *Tit* and *djed* in two parts; painted
    eyes

Condition
Good. Completely restored in 1976.

Provenance
Western Thebes; Deir el-Medina; tomb No. 1 of Sennudjem

Date
Sethos I, or perhaps Ramses II

Bibliography
Cairo Museum, *A Brief Description of the Principal Monuments,*
    Nos. 2001 and 2003
Toda/Daressy, *ASAE* XX (1920), pp. 151-156
Bruyère, *FIFAO* 1924 to 1930: 1924/5, pp. 190-192, figs. 126, 127;
    1928, pp. 134-135, Pl. XIII; 1930, Pl. XXXII

Desroches Noblecourt *et alii*
Catalogue of the Ramsès le Grand exhibition, Paris, 1976,
    No. XXXV, pp. 164-167

According to the information now available on the funerary equipment of the pharaohs, the latter were buried, in the New Kingdom and especially beginning in the 19th dynasty, with extraordinary trappings. The treasure of Tutankhamun has provided an intact example. It is known that in the Ramses dynasty, the approach was exactly the same. The mummy, accompanied by a multitude of jewels and amulets and wrapped in a shroud under a gold plastron-mask, was placed in a solid gold sarcophagus which itself was set in another gold-plated sarcophagus. In turn, this was inserted into a third golden coffin, supported by a funerary bed which was also golden and bore a lion's head. With its load, the bed was placed in a granite funerary case, protected by a fine veil stitched with gold rosettes (the stars), decorating a sort of canopy supported by a golden wood frame. This already elaborate system was enclosed in four golden wooden chapels fitting into one another. The whole was then placed in the funerary chamber–the last room in a sumptuous tomb dug into the bowels of the rock.

The funerary trappings of lords or craftsmen of Deir el-Medina in no way compared with the riches of the royal house of eternity. A chapel, decorated with reliefs and paintings evoking scenes from daily life which were interpreted by transposing their message, dominated a well dug in the ground leading to a tomb which, beginning with the middle of the 18th dynasty, was decorated with paintings generally showing vignettes from the Book of the Dead.

Sennudjem, the leader of this great family of craftsmen, had an outer sarcophagus, not of gold, but of stuccoed and painted wood, to which had been added a harmoniously sculpted face and hands crossed on the chest. His sarcophagi, in two parts, were nestled in one another and placed in an immense wooden funerary case on a sleigh, darkened with yellow gold hieroglyphs, now in the Cairo Museum. The cover of the other sarcophagus is exhibited here. It shows the deceased in his shroud. The wrappings which hold the cloth are represented by a large median line of hieroglyphs and three horizontal lines perpendicular to the first. Sennudjem's hands hold the knot of Isis (*tit*) and the Osiris pillar (*djed*), whose upper part has disappeared. The face, a magnificent, idealized portrait, is painted ochre red. The eyebrows and eyes are black and white.

Sennudjem's stately wig with twisted locks and curls represents the contemporary civilian headdress. At the top of his head, the image of the goddess Nephthys, with yellow flesh and dressed in a long tunic with blue straps, is shown kneeling. The goddess Isis is recognized under the feet of the sarcophagus, her body encased in a net. It was the place of the goddesses, sisters of Osiris, watching over the dead. Sennudjem's forehead is adorned with an imposing floral headband. He wears the small goatee of a lord. On his chest, the broad necklace with seven rows of pearls and two rows of drops is made of floral elements and protects the deceased. A second necklace, with mandrakes, descends each side on the arms of the deceased, passing beneath his hands.

The image of the goddess Nut with wings outstretched dominates all the lower part of the body where three groups of vignettes are interspersed among the wrappings: first, the two silhouettes of Anubis, guardian and guide of the dead, stretched out on his *naos*, then two protective goddesses, their hands on the image of the solar circuit and, finally, the two most attractive paintings in the decoration of the sarcophagus. At the height of the ankles and feet and arranged so that the deceased may see them, Sennudjem himself receives the libation of the sycamore goddess in a vessel she holds in her hand. An important detail is the fact that Sennudjem, in these two parallel representations, has a black wig in one and a white wig in the other.

Detail

34

Cover-board of the mummy of Sennudjem

Catalogue entry number of the Cairo Museum: 27,308

Dimensions
Height: 1.75 m
Width at the shoulders: 0.443 m
Depth at the base: 0.21 m

Medium
Stuccoed and painted wood (black, white, brick red, red, yellow, green); the back is covered with a shiny black material resembling pitch; the top is partially covered with varnish which has yellowed.

Technique
Face and feet set in (ankles).

Condition
Restored and repainted (1975)

Provenance
Western Thebes; Deir el-Medina; tomb No. 1 of Sennudjem

Date
Late in the reign of Sethos I or first half of the reign of Ramses II

Bibliography
Porter-Moss I-1, p. 4

Desroches Noblecourt *et alii*
Catalogue of the Ramsès le Grand exhibition, Paris, 1976, No. XXXVI, pp. 168-169

Beginning in the 19th dynasty, i.e., from the Ramesside period, the evolution of funerary concepts and their expression introduced a sarcophagus into funerary trappings in the "costume of the living". It is among those which show the deceased in his shroud. This is the case with this cover-board bearing the likeness of a man with nude torso wearing a long, white, pleated festival loincloth, with his hands on his thighs. He is adorned only with his "broad necklace". His wig is much smaller—the long locks are not layered and its form recalls the appearance of the previous headdress. The beard is somewhat larger and, looking at the face, one sees the features of a young man. He is youthful in his coming rebirth. No funerary representation clutters the portrait of Sennudjem. On his wrists, he wears pearl bracelets; his feet are bare and between his legs is an inscription which recalls that he is "the servant of the Place of Truth, west of Thebes, Sennudjem, the justified". The only allusion to the rites here is beneath the feet where the silhouette of the goddess Isis raises her arms. From them are suspended the signs of life.

Detail

35

Cover of the sarcophagus of Lady Isis

Catalogue entry number of the Cairo museum: 27,309

Dimensions
Height (length): 1.935 m
Thickness (foot level): 0.318 m
Max. width: 0.47 m

Medium
Wood covered with a fine fabric soaked with stucco and painted;
    varnish; white, green, ochre red and yellow, green, blue, and black

Technique
Cover made of several pieces. At head level, there are three
    superimposed layers of wood. The mask is fastened by two
    wooden pegs, inserted at cheek height. Feet and arms are set
    in, as are the accessories: earrings, amulet. Painted eyes. The
    inside of the cover is covered with black varnish. Four pairs of
    tenons fit into corresponding mortises of the container to adjust
    the cover to it.

Condition
Generally very good. Polychromy of the face altered and scaling in
    several places on the cover. Restorations by injection (1976). The
    amulet (?) held in the left hand has been lost. The small toe
    of the right foot is broken; the ring around the thumb is
    damaged.

Provenance
Deir el-Medina, tomb No. 1 of Sennudjem

Date
Ramses II period

Bibliography
Maspero, *BIE*, 2nd series, No. 7, 1886, Cairo, 1887, p. 204
    (The author erroneously attributes the sarcophagus of Isis to
    Iyneferty)
Vernier, *BIFAO*, VIII, 1911, p. 18, Pl. II (for earrings)
Hayes, *Scepter*, II, pp. 414 and 416, Fig. 264 (for comparison with
    Iyneferty sarcophagi)

Desroches Noblecourt *et alii*
Catalogue of the Ramsès le Grand exhibition, Paris, 1976,
    No. XXXVII, pp. 170-171

Sculpted in wood and covered with painted stucco to which linen has been pasted is the cover of the sarcophagus of Lady Isis who married one of the sons of Sennudjem—the craftsman Khabekhnet. Encasing even the feet, it is placed on the mummy, above the plastron. The mummy is in the "costume of the living", but in the attitude of mummified women, i.e., with one hand resting on the chest, the other stretched out towards the knee. She wears the long headdress of Ramesside ladies, prominent earrings of two types—rings and cabochons—an opulent floral headband, broken above the forehead by a lotus flower (sometimes framed with buds) descending towards the face. Often, as is the case here, the fine locks of natural hair framing the face appear under the flowing headdress.

Wearing a necklace so broad it becomes a plastron, Lady Isis is dressed in a fine linen robe, rather narrow at ankle height and scalloped with two flares on the front. The sleeves are puffed; the prominent chest under the plastron is as if protected by two jewels in the shape of cabochons. The folds of the robe are suggested by sorts of ochre-red graduated shadows. The flesh of the deceased who, when shown alive, is shaded a light ochre, here is red. The lady wears several pieces of jewelry. She has a triple green ring on each of the four fingers of the right hand, bracelets made of small green, ochre and yellow bars, another consisting of green and blue diamond shapes, and two new forearm ornaments, worn on the bias. Green and blue pearls are seen on them. Undeniably, these are jewels found in a still more sumptuous version in the images of Nefertari in her tomb in the Valley of the Queens.

Other ornaments have disappeared but the fastening holes recall their locations on the wrists and on the thumb of the right hand. Against her chest, the lady holds in one hand a genuine cluster of branches of ivy bearing fruit. With the other hand, she holds it against her right thigh. On her white robe, plants stand out remarkably in dark green. Ivy was one of the plants of Osiris. The deceased, while using this climbing plant as a decoration, also sought to benefit from the symbolic message it conveyed. As with the cover-board of Sennudjem, the image of Isis is shown beneath the feet, but standing and dressed in a red robe. In each hand, she holds a sign of life. From her elbows hang two amulets in the form of *djed* pillars.

The plastron of Lady Isis as well as her large funerary case are in the collection of the Cairo Museum. The whole of the ritual trappings were placed in the tomb of her father-in-law, Sennudjem, next to that of her husband, Khabekhnet. When the tomb was discovered (February, 1884), it provided so many similar elements the Egyptian government authorized a sale to some foreign museums. The Metropolitan Museum of Art in New York acquired one of the funerary cases of Iyneferty, the wife of Sennudjem.

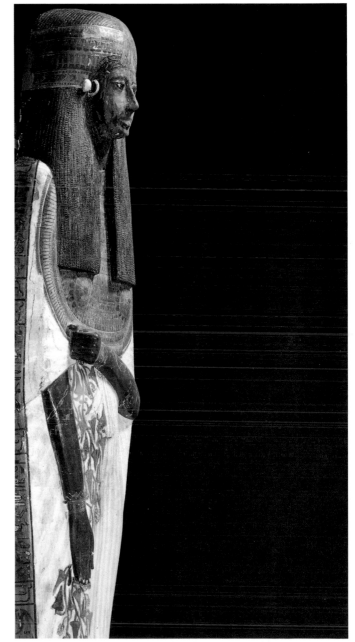

Detail

36

Cover-board of the mummy of Piay

Provisional catalogue number of the Cairo Museum: 5-12-25-3

Dimensions
Total length: 1.79 m
Width: 0.43 m

Medium
Stuccoed wood painted black, white, ochre red and yellow; a vestige of fabric is pasted on the back.

Technique
Hands and face set in

Condition
Painting on the face restored; assembly restored

Provenance
Unknown

Date
Probably Ramses II, based on the style

Bibliography
Desroches Noblecourt *et alii*
Catalogue of the Ramsès le Grand exhibition, Paris, 1976, No. XXXVIII, pp. 172-173

This "mummy cover" does not belong to a member of Sennudjem's family, yet the person in the "costume of the living" is worthy of interest. The style is comparable to that of the first part of the 19th dynasty. With pure features and an aquiline nose, the face has a somewhat severe mouth but the expression is toned down by the softness of the physiognomy. The wig is not far divorced from the classical shape of that of Sennudjem; however, the floral headband passes well above the bangs on the forehead. The lotus flower in the centre is in relief. The man wears a tunic with wide, pleated sleeves which covers his entire torso, but the location of the navel, for ritual reasons, is emphatically marked. A sort of pleated scarf surrounds his loins, crosses and returns to the front in a short flap and is again pleated as it falls. The feet are bare and the jewelry is unostentatious.

Large, round earrings are exceptionally worn by the man. Of Oriental origin, they appear only in the New Kingdom and seem reserved for women and children. Two pairs of bracelets suggesting gold jewels are on the wrists and the forearms. The flesh of the man is dark ochre red, in striking contrast to the white of the robe and the black of the wig. The small goatee has disappeared but the fastening hole remains. The closed hands must have held the knot of Isis (*tit*) and the Osiris pillar (*djed*).

According to the inscription engraved on the front of the skirt, the man is called Piay. The name was a frequent one at the time. On the other hand, however, his title is indeed rare. He claims to be "chief merchant of the Prince". Trade, at least until the 18th dynasty, was the prerogative of civil servants in Egypt. However, starting with the Amarnian period when a large number of foreigners was welcomed to Egypt, we learn from texts that these merchants—intermediaries who worked for the temples as well as for civilians—were Syrians. In the city of Tell el-Amarna, digs have uncovered the store of a Mycenaean merchant. From the Orient, these merchants also introduced into Egypt cereals, bovidae, splendid textiles that later were the glory of Damascus and even young "slaves". They also traded with the heads of caravans who brought precious wood and spices from faraway countries or aromatics from countries to the east and the south, copper from the Semitic mines of Timna, north of Eilat, and lapis lazuli from Bactria.

The person was probably important. Perhaps he was even of Syrian origin, as his earrings would suggest. He was close to the royal house.

Detail

37

● Techniques and daily occupations
Level in the form of a square

Catalogue entry number of the Cairo Museum: 27,258

Dimensions
Length of preserved branch: 0.366 m
Length of broken branch: 0.203 m
Length of cross bar at base: 0.222 m
Height of plummet: 0.053

Medium
Painted wooden frame; limestone plummet. Background painted
   yellow; red outlines of the texts; blue hieroglyphs

Technique
Assembly of three small wooden rules

Condition
One of the branches is broken at the cross bar; restored in 1975; the
   string is modern.

Provenance
Western Thebes, Deir el-Medina; tomb No. 1 of Sennudjem

Date
Probably the first half of the reign of Ramses II

Bibliography
Porter-Moss I-1, p. 4
Capart, *CdE* 16 (1941), pp. 200-201, Fig. 5

Desroches Noblecourt *et alii*
Catalogue of the Ramsès le Grand exhibition, Paris, 1976,
   No. XXXIX, pp. 174-175

This humble work instrument must long have served
Egyptian craftsmen and even the architects who built
so many marvels. We continue to admire these great
builders whose tools are known to have been so simple but at the same time so effective, proof of their
extreme skill and not of jealously guarded mysteries.
Also known is their cubit–a royal cubit equals 0.52 m–
a rule graduated in various subdivisions up to the
width of the finger which itself was divided into
fractions.

The scant equipment includes the level in the
form of a square. The right angle was the starting
point for a line specifying verticality. At the end of it
was a heart-shaped counterweight. On the cross bar,
at the front and back, reference marks were engraved
in the middle as well as on the diagonal of the upper
angle. These reference marks obviously made it possible to check the horizontality of a surface when the
string with the counterweight passed exactly over it.

These are the only indications the instrument left
behind since the inscriptions adorning the sides of the
"pyramid" consist of invocations to the god Ptah and
the god Rehorakhty-Atum, made by Sennudjem in
order to become a luminous Spirit in the sky and powerful on earth.

Catalogue entry number of the Cairo Museum: 27,260

Dimensions
Height of board: 0.486 m
Length of upper shelf: 0.08 m
Length of lower shelf: 0.079 m
Height of plummet: 0.055 m

Medium
Painted wood; limestone plummet

Technique
Assembly by tenons and mortises

Condition
Yellow background; red outlines of the text; black hieroglyphs.
    Restored in 1975

Provenance
Western Thebes, Deir el-Medina; tomb No. 1 of Sennudjem

Date
Probably first half of the reign of Ramses II

Bibliography
Porter-Moss I-1, p. 4

Desroches Noblecourt *et alii*
Catalogue of the Ramsès le Grand exhibition, Paris, 1976,
    No. XL, pp. 176

The object, also made of wood, painted yellow and bearing an inscription in black outlined in red, is marked with the name of the same owner as that of the preceding object. One may read: "the servant of the Master of the Two Lands, Sennudjem, the justified". The object is a rather highly perfected plumb-line; it was not used, like the preceding object, to check whether a surface was perfectly horizontal, but to ensure that a wall was exactly perpendicular at its base. The string passes from the top of the rule through a hole at the end of the upper horizontal shelf, then descends vertically to brush against a second shelf in the same direction. It ends naturally in a heart-shaped plummet. The job was done by leaning the rule against the wall to be checked. When the string touched the edge of the lower shelf, the wall was completely vertical.

Catalogue entry number of the Cairo Museum: 38,642

Dimensions
Total height: 1.05 m
Height of column with its arms: 0.92 m
Height of limestone base: 0.08 m
Diameter of base: 0.265

Lamp
Height: 0.07 m
Length with handle: 0.245 m
Length without handle: 0.205 m
Width: 0.181

Medium
Limestone base; (red) painted wooden support; copper or bronze
    lamp; traces of grease and ashes; fragment of an undetermined
    material; wooden stick

Technique
Hammered vessel; base roughly squared

Provenance
Western Thebes, Deir el-Medina; tomb No. 8 of Kha. Schiaparelli
    digs in 1906

Date
Middle of the 18th dynasty (second half of the 15th century BC)
    (Kha lived under Tuthmosis IV and Amenophis III)

Bibliography
Schiaparelli, *Relazione*, Vol. II, p. 15, Fig. 15 and p. 144, Fig. 127
Mentioned in: Bruyère, *FIFAO* 3 (1926), p. 15, Fig. 9 and *FIFAO* 16
    (1939), p.209
Encyclopédie photo, p. 24, No. 94

On workmen's lighting, see: Černý, *The Valley of the Kings*,
    Bibliothèque d'Étude 61 (1973), p. 43 and ff.

Desroches Noblecourt *et alii*
Catalogue of the Ramsès le Grand exhibition, Paris, 1976,
    No. XLIII, pp. 186-188

This object would be at home in a modern architect's apartment as a tribute to one of his remote ancestors, Chief of Works Kha.

Though the lamp dates to the 18th dynasty, between the reigns of Amenophis II and Amenophis III, quite numerous fragments from similar lamps found in the workmen's village of the royal necropolis prove it must have been commonly used in homes. It appeared useful to include it among objects dealing with the life setting of craftsmen at Deir el-Medina where Kha lived. His tomb contained funerary furniture which now, almost in its entirety, is displayed at the Turin museum.

The apparatus closest to contemporary living-room lamps, it is in unique condition. Egyptian lamps took several forms–they could be placed on the ground, on stools or on small tables–but the profile of the central part was always the same and did not resemble the small lamps which appear in the Greek and Roman periods and which had a narrow outlet for the flame. There was also a torch system of classical form or with a large, triangular volume.

The most humble lamps were terracotta cups used extensively by workers laboring in burial vaults. They were filled with oil or a type of grease in which a wick, made of a strip of twisted linen, or sometimes a papyrus core, was soaked. The *ostraca* from Deir el-Medina describing supplies given to workers to carry out their jobs reveal that quantities of salt had to be placed in the oil to prevent the lamp from smoking.

Kha's lamp is made of three parts–a limestone base, roughly half-spherical in shape (at the top of the curve was placed a column in the shape of a papyri stem marked with three characteristic ribs); the capital recalling the umbrella-shape of a blooming plant and five stria suggesting the ligatures which surrounded not a papyrus but a bundle of papyrus; the central element of the lamp was dominated at the top of the umbrella shape by three flared arms, fastened at the top; on the arms was placed the third, essential part– the receptacle of light.

The light itself, probably made of bronze, suggests the general appearance of a fish with a swollen body, the head marked by a spout and a horizontal caudal fin. In the bottom of the vessel is still a sort of compact grease—a whitish material in which vestiges of burnt ingredients remain, including a piece of substance probably used to scent the air. A small wooden stick, perhaps used to mix the salt and oil, was stuck in the grease.

Catalogue entry number of the Cairo Museum: JE.6269

Dimensions
Height: 0.20 m
Width: 0.14 m
Length: 0.36 m

Medium
Wood

Technique
In two pieces

Condition
Good

Provenance
Gourna

Date
New Kingdom

Bibliography
Nota bene:
Objects 9, 12 and those numbered from 40 to 63 were included in the exhibition as the catalogue went to press. Though their descriptions and the archaeological comments about them could be prepared within a short deadline, there was, unfortunately, insufficient time for appropriate research. Consequently, and with the exception of some objects, the technical descriptions of objects bearing the numbers mentioned above are based almost solely on the data kindly provided by curators of the Cairo Museum.

From the Old Kingdom, at least, major funerary furniture included a low bed on which the deceased could rest. Most of the time, a small accessory, called a headrest, was placed on the mattress. There is no absolute proof that the headrest was commonly used for sleeping since its comfort leaves much to be desired. However, it may have been necessary when an Egyptian, wearing a heavy wig, wished to rest. In any case, this is what may be seen on the representations of small, nude female figurines stretched out on beds and wearing cumbersome headdresses, inspired by that of the goddess Hathor.

Without doubt, the primary use of these headrests was probably to support the nape of the mummy's neck so that the head did not detach from the trunk for the body had to be integrally preserved. The headrests were also used to help at the time of rebirth. They suggest the two mountains on the horizon where the sun rises at dawn each morning. Certainly, the skull of the deceased was assimilated with this idea at the time of eternal resurrection. To encourage a dull sun to shine, symbolized by the head of the deceased, the presence of small round papyri, called *hypocephali* by Egyptologists and covered with magical signs to awaken the drowsy star, are noted during the last millenium of Egyptian history.

The headrests were provided with ornaments recalling the role they were to play. Under the curve, two hands, which seem to reinforce it, are sometimes seen. They suggest the gesture of the god Shu who raises the sky. One of Tutankhamun's beautiful ivory headrests shows us the god himself in action. On each side, at the base, the two lions of the horizon complete the scene. Elsewhere, flanking the small central column, appear Isis and Nephthys, protectors of the deceased.

Here, spirits bearing a knife are engraved. Their role is to defend the deceased against attacks by the Cunning. The god Bes himself, with the same weapons, watches over the sleeping person who is to experience new birth.

41

Bowl with flowers and fish

Catalogue entry number of the Cairo Museum: 63,677

Dimensions
Upper diameter: 0.17 m

Medium
Glazed terracotta

Technique
Quite fine grain; good quality glaze

Condition
Scale on the rim shows the pink terracotta underneath

Provenance
Deir el-Medina

Date
Early 19th dynasty (?)

Bibliography
(cf. *Nota bene* at the bottom of the technical description of object 40)
Desroches Noblecourt, *Un lac de turquoise*, in Monuments et
　　Mémoires, PIOT, XLVII, Paris, 1953, pp. 1-34
Strauss, *Die Nunschale: eine Gefässegruppe des Neuen Reiches*,
　　Munich/Berlin, 1974

The small, bowl-shaped vessel with short, flared walls is decorated with black drawings on a magnificent, luminous turquoise blue background. The lip, serving as a rim, is enhanced by a wide black line. The decoration is made up of the image of a small quadrangular basin at the centre surrounded by a double lip–the first is made by a strip defined by two black lines and a much larger frame decorated with small squares alternately shown in black and blue. In the centre of the basin, black overlapping lines suggest water. The inside periphery of the basin, evoking a pond, is filled with the representation of plants and animals which it must have actually contained. Two large *bultis* (*tilapia nilotica*) are shown swimming peacefully. From their "jaws" projects an undulated stem ending in a lotus bud. In the spaces separating them, one can see a plant group of two half-open lotuses framing a sort of lyriform palm leaf from which spring petals edged with two forms of foliage. The decoration indicates an Oriental influence. Near the right lotus are a bud and another more open lotus, curved to follow the form of the vessel.

This type of cuppel, which must have been used by Egyptians to drink water or wine, was placed in tombs above all to provide the deceased with the water of youth which would ensure eternal rebirth. It is therefore at one and the same time the primeval water in which the disincarnated one is supposed to be immersed and from which he will be reborn in the East of the World, in the form of the small fish of survival, bearing the lotus from which the sun appears.

42

Slender necked vase of Sennudjem

Catalogue entry number of the Cairo Museum: J.27,216

Dimensions
Height: 0.33 m

Medium
Terracotta

Technique
Pottery made on a lathe and hand-painted

Condition
Very good but the handle is broken

Provenance
Deir el-Medina

Date
19th dynasty

Bibliography
(cf. *Nota bene* at the bottom of the technical description of object 40)

The belly of the vessel quite accurately suggests the shape of the hieroglyph of the Egyptian heart, fitted with two small rounded handles on the sides. It simultaneously alludes to a human torso—alabaster vases found in Tutankhamun's tomb bear the mark of female breasts. Here, this reminder is represented by a wide necklace with a double row of blue lotus petals separated by red strips and ending at the base in a pendant in the shape of a large lotus, flanked by buds and standing out against the white background. The petals of the necklace are marked with graduated colors from blue-green to yellow and including white.

The high, straight neck is bordered at the top with a slightly protruding lip. It is decorated mainly with three floral friezes at the top and base, with the representation of two garlands made of lotus petals sewn on a ribbon and, at the centre, with a colored area where mandrake fruit is shown.

Bibliography
(cf. *Nota bene* at the bottom of the technical description of object 40)

This chest must have been among the precious accessories of the head of the household of Pharaoh's best craftsmen early in the Ramesside period.

The lateral uprights end in a form of square-section leg of a height almost equal to that of the rectangular box. The cover, bordered by the two slightly protruding lateral uprights of the object, is maintained on one of the large sides by two pegs on which it pivots.

The location of the two buttons opposite each other simplified the installation of sealed ligatures–the classical easy method of closing the box.

This type of chest nearly always had partitions in it, facilitating the arrangement of jewels and other precious objects belonging to the owner.

44

Ovoid vase bearing the names of Ramses II

Catalogue entry number of the Cairo Museum: 46.712

Dimensions
Height: 0.266 m

Medium
Alabaster inlaid with blue and red colored pastes

Condition
Nicked on the lip

Provenance
Biban el-Muluk (Valley of the Kings)

Date
19th dynasty

Bibliography
(cf. *Nota bene* at the bottom of the technical description of object 40)

It seems evident that this lovely alabaster, inlaid with blue paste and engraved with the two names of Ramses II opposite one another, must at some time have been part of the stock of royal furniture. On the belly may be read: "The Lord of the Two Lands, Usimaare-Setepenre", on the right, and opposite, on the left: "The Lord of Apparitions Ramessu-mery-Amun". On the other side of the belly is a trace of a hieratic graffito.

The fact it was found in the Valley of the Kings prompts the belief that this vessel could be one of the rare vestiges of funerary equipment forgotten among the rubbish when the tomb was looted in Antiquity. It also could have been buried in a rocky hiding-place of the Valley because of its use during Pharaoh's funeral.

Whatever the case, this vessel with an ovoid belly, which ends in the hemmed opening of a wide lip, was certainly not a vase in the modern sense of the word. It must have been closed with a stopper which fitted into the spout and whose upper part could either have been flat in the form of a blooming lotus or dominated by a graceful human or animal image. It undoubtedly contained rare products such as unguents or very precious and expensive plant essences which often came from abroad, or only fabrics which had been used during funeral rites before the tomb.

45

Door of Sennudjem's burial chamber

Catalogue entry number of the Cairo Museum: 27,303

Dimensions
Total height: approx. 1.35 m
Height of panel: 1.17 m (approx.)
Width: 0.78 m (approx.)

Medium
Stuccoed, painted wood; yellow background; decoration on the outer
   side: white background; details: black, white, red, green, blue,
   yellow; black hieroglyphs with red outlines

Technique
Wooden parts joined by tenons

Condition
The wood is cracked; restored in 1975

Provenance
Western Thebes; Deir el-Medina, tomb No. 1 of Sennudjem

Date
Probably the first half of the reign of Ramses II

Bibliography
Porter-Moss I-1, p. 3
Bruyère, *La tombe n° 1 de Sennedjem, MIFAO* 88 (1959), pp. 21-23,
   pp. 52-53, Pl. XVI-XVII
Koenigsberger, *Die Konstruktion der ägyptischen Tür, Äg. Forsch.* 2
   (1936) Barguet, *Le Livre des Morts des Anciens Égyptiens*,
   1967
Needler, *JEA* 39 (1953), pp. 60-75 (*senet* game)
Piankoff, *The Wandering of the Soul*, Part III, *The Egyptian Game of
   Draughts*, Bollingen, Series XL.6, Princeton, 1972
Kendall, *Passing through the Netherworld: The Meaning and Play
   of Senet, An Ancient Funerary Game*
Pusch, *Das Senet Brettspiel in Alten Ägypten*, Pl. 1,
   Das inschriftliche und archäologische Material, Munich/Berlin

Desroches Noblecourt *et alii*
Catalogue of the Ramsès le Grand exhibition, Paris, 1976,
   No. XLIV, pp. 189-193

Here we see the only door of a Theban burial chamber which is well preserved and decorated. Made of several wooden panels held in a frame, it was, at its discovery, still attached to its limestone door frame, unpillaged, in Maspero's time. It was even locked with a sort of palm tree lock consisting of a door bolt operated by a small cord which crossed the door and was embedded in stone. (A similar system still exists in some old peasant houses in Upper Egypt.) A block of wood on the outer face of the door served to support the bolt and was perforated by two metal rings. The small cord was fastened to the limestone casing through a clay seal with a stamp of the image of Anubis, guardian and guide of the dead. Two hinge pins are driven into the sockets of the lintel and the threshold. The device made it possible to open the door for the burial of each member of the family.

The two outer and inner sides of the door were decorated with the bright colors of the Egyptian palette. All the freshness of the coloring remains. The background of the outer side is white and the two superimposed sections, corresponding to two paintings, dominated at the top by the image of the sky, do not cover the entire surface. The inner side, which faced the burial chamber, the domain of the mummy, is yellow like the color of the gold room of royal burial chambers. The decoration covers the panel.

The outer side, which faced the world of the living, was adorned with a representation of members of the family worshipping before the gods of the world of the dead. On the lower section, closest to the earthly world, appear the reproduction of Ptah-Sokar-Osiris, escorted by Isis, the Great, Mistress of the Sky. A libation vessel, crowned with a lotus bouquet, placed on a stool, separates them from the seven sons of Sennudjem arriving two by two and preceded by the eldest, Khabekhnet, who has no floral stem in his hand.

On the upper section is Osiris, wearing a magnificent *atef* and holding his scepters and the cane *was*. The goddess Maat places her hand on one of his shoulders. In front of him, the same small piece of furniture separates him from Sennudjem, wearing his pleated, full loincloth and long black wig, his torso nude, raising his arms in adoration. Behind him is his wife Iyneferty with a long wig through which an earring may be seen. The wig is round on the cheek and dominated by a fragrant cone, the same as that worn by Sennudjem but stitched with a lotus in front. Her long robe, also full, is pleated, as are the sleeves. Her daughter, who is smaller, is behind her. She wears the same robe and headdress but her robe falls off the shoulder. Lady Iyneferty makes a gesture of adoration while her daughter, Irunefer, touches the flap of her wig. Both carry long necked ovoid vessels which may have contained wine. They wear yoke-necklaces with heavy counterweights in back.

Facing the burial chamber, the panel is covered with 11 lines of text dominated by a typically Egyptian representation evoking the deceased, accompanied by lyneferty, playing the *senet* game. They are both sheltered by reeds, likely of papyrus, called *seh*, ligatured at the angles and also placed on a papyrus mat. In front of them is a well-laden offering table where ovoid vessels and round breads, fruit baskets, figs, vegetables and cucumbers are heaped on a papyrus mat. Below, four cabbage lettuces and two bottles of milk complete the more or less symbolic food. The deceased and his wife are on seats recalling those found in the family burial chamber. Their wigs are still more voluminous than on the other side of the door. The woman entwines a shoulder and an arm of her husband with her own arms. Sennudjem holds a long ceremonial handkerchief in one hand and rests the other hand on one of the ten pawns of the game, which are alternately white and red and of different shapes. At the foot of the stool is a large knuckle bone used to play the game.

The Egyptians certainly must have enjoyed playing *senet*. The rules are still difficult to reconstruct. The game must have been a cross between the goose game, the snakes and ladders game and checkers. In any event, it appears certain that it had broad funerary use and was essential to the deceased in the quest for eternity. The text shown under the representation is made up of the last paragraph of Chapter 72 and the first paragraph of Chapter 17 of the Book of the Dead:
"As for he who knows this book on earth, or he on the sarcophagus of whom it is written, he will appear one day under all the aspects he will like. He will return to his place without being repulsed. He will be given bread and beer and he will be fed meat from the altars of Osiris. He will be able to go towards the Cyperus Fields according to the decree (of Osiris) and there he will be given barley and spelt. Then, he will flourish as he did on earth and he will do what he likes like these gods (which are in the Duat). This (book) is truly effective (thousands of times)."

The opening of Chapter 17 notes:
"Beginning of transfigurations and illuminations of the exit and of the return in the necropolis. Be a Luminous one in the beautiful West, so as to go out in the day and do all the transformations one desires (having) played *senet,* seated under the (papyrus) shelter, (then) go out as a living-soul, by Osiris, the servant of the Place of Truth, Sennudjem, the justified, and his wife, the mistress of the house, lyneferty, the justified."

The impact of these texts is thus understood. It is also seen that Sennudjem plays against an invisible adversary and must win from him passage through the door in order to gain the possibility of appearing in the day. He may come in any form over the entire period during which he must undoubtedly follow a long trail. Having passed into the kingdom of Osiris (yesterday, as the texts of Chapter 17 of the Book of the Dead say), he must become incorporated with that of Re (i.e., tomorrow, according to the same Chapter 17). It should be noted that Sennudjem's wife does not take part in the game and is satisfied to hold him in her arms.

46

Senet game

Catalogue entry number of the Cairo Museum: J.21,462

Dimensions
Length: 0.265 m
Width: 0.078 m

Medium
Bone and ebony wood; pawns of glazed terracotta

Technique
Inlays and pasting of bone elements in the wooden framework; sliding-
    drawer

Condition
Some squares have been repaired; small elements missing

Provenance
Dra Abu el-Naga

Date
New Kingdom

Bibliography
(cf. *Nota bene* at the bottom of the technical description of object
    40.)
See references concerning the door of Sennudjem's burial cham-
    ber (45).

The Egyptians of Antiquity, like those of today, always enjoyed games as a pastime. There is not a single inhabitant of the Nile who does not know how to play backgammon (*taôla*)! From the first dynasty, one finds in tombs disks imitating the coiling of the body of a long snake, the *mehen*. The coils are marked by small squares. Very quickly, this distraction was reproduced on the walls of funerary sanctuaries. From the begin-ning and thanks to two examples which have been preserved—one in the Leiden Museum, the other in the Louvre—one understands that this snakes and ladders game was truly at the origin of the goose game. In fact, if the head of the serpent is shown in the centre and at the beginning of the course, the end of its body is replaced by the head of a goose, the solar animal.

The snakes game, then the goose game, are found in the West, millennia later, the first preserved in Anglo-Saxon countries (snakes and ladders). The sec-ond is the well-known coiling of the goose game of the Latins which, legend has it, was "renewed by the Greeks". When children in schoolyards play hop-scotch by pushing a stone to go to hell or heaven, they do not realize they have traced on the ground the ves-tiges of the "small *senet*". And when starting with the Renaissance, the canons of the chapter of cathedrals—that of Reims, for example—gathered on the labyrinth of the parvis, on Pentecost Day, they unknowingly repeated the actions of the first players of the goose game who sought to overcome all the trials encoun-tered on the body of the serpent in order to come out of the beak of the goose, like the new sun.

The game quickly appeared in its classical form, shown on the two sides of a long triangular box fitted with a drawer in which the pawns and various acces-sories were placed. On one side, there are 30 squares in three rows of ten, on which the pawns are moved. The last five, in general, are marked with hieroglyphs, the last clearly suggesting the sun. But one of the squares bears the three signs of water; it is still recalled by the symbolism of the well in the goose game.

On the other side, the "small *senet*" roughly recalls hopscotch.

Fragmentary texts relating to this pastime do not make it possible to reconstruct the game entirely, but everything points to the probability that it was, in fact, used by the living. It was nevertheless essential to the survival of the deceased, allowing the dead to cross the different phases of their "purgatory", represented

by the doors they had to cross. That is why kings as well as their subjects are shown playing the game with an invisible adversary, seeking to vanquish him through the skill provided by the purity of their early actions and on their own right.

There are ten pawns, differentiated by their respective colors and shapes. The most elaborate and the most precious games could, for half the pieces, consist of pawns often modeled in the image of prisoners with their hands tied behind their backs—those in the camp of the adversary, naturally. Those on the good side were sometimes adorned with heads of the god Bes who protected births.

The game was played by the rolling of dice and also, probably, based on the different sides of small sticks thrown in a certain manner.

Another pastime, also prized by the Egyptians, was that of the Hippopotamus with progress towards the various stations forming extremely complicated circuits. Pegs with the heads of dogs with straight or drooping ears on them were placed in holes marking the course.

The game exhibited here is inlaid with bone plates occupying the place of the squares on which pawns are moved over the large surface made up of 30 divisions. The visible side wall is filled with three rectangular areas. On the right-hand area is a sphinx with a human head in relief. On the middle one is preserved the central part and left side of a composition of Oriental influence, composed of the Tree of Life—here a lyriform palm leaf—flanked by two capridae standing against the plant they seem prepared to nibble. (Only the left ibex is preserved.)

47

Sennudjem's small coffin, formerly containing mummified viscera

Catalogue entry number of the Cairo Museum: SR.41 = C.4251

Dimensions
Length: 0.34 m

Medium
Limestone

Technique
In two parts

Condition
Very good

Provenance
Deir el-Medina

Date
19th dynasty

Bibliography
(cf. *Nota bene* at the bottom of the technical description of object 40.)

To preserve them from decomposition, the Egyptians mummified the bodies of their deceased. They began by extracting the brain and the viscera. Once the remains were relieved of their fat after being soaked in baths aromatized with natron, only the heart and the kidneys—"god probes the heart and the kidneys", according to the stele in the Gulbenkian collection in Lisbon—were put back inside the body.

The viscera were in turn treated and mummified and, starting with the Middle Kingdom, were placed in high-bellied vessels, crowned with a cover bearing a human face. They were called canopic jars by the first Egyptologists who compared their form to the vessel which the pilot of Menelas had worshipped in the city of Canopus in the Delta. As of the Ramesside period, the vessels were given covers of four different forms—a human head, a falcon head, a dog head, and a baboon head. They suggest the four sons of Horus—Imsety, Qebsennuef, Duamutef and Hapy—while the four bellies were under the aegis of the four protective goddesses of the mummy—Isis, Nephthys, Neith and Selket (cf. Khons' funerary container, 48).

Sovereigns had canopic jars to preserve human heads. If one refers to the tomb of Tutankhamun, in the room next to the hall where the body was placed, a magnificent chest on a sleigh was made of gilded wood. Inside, an alabaster sanctuary contained four vases, also of alabaster, with human heads, within which were four cloisonné gold sarcophagi bearing the image of Tutankhamun protecting the mummified viscera of the young king.

In light of this, one may then deduce that the manufacture of Sennudjem's coffin closely paralleled that of royal furniture and that, in this context, the vase for his viscera was prepared by imitating from afar the style of Pharaoh. Here, we see the faithful reduction of a small, mummy-shaped sarcophagus, painted white and crossed with yellow wrappings, outlined in red and with black hieroglyphic inscriptions. Sennudjem's names and titles appear on it along with those of the protective spirits and the cardinal points favorable to the peace of the deceased. The red face of the figure with large, protruding ears is framed with an ample funerary wig imitating the royal gold and lapis lazuli inlays which here are merely painted. The huge lotus neck-piece protrudes from the wig and the hands crossed on the chest. The face, intact, is extremely well executed.

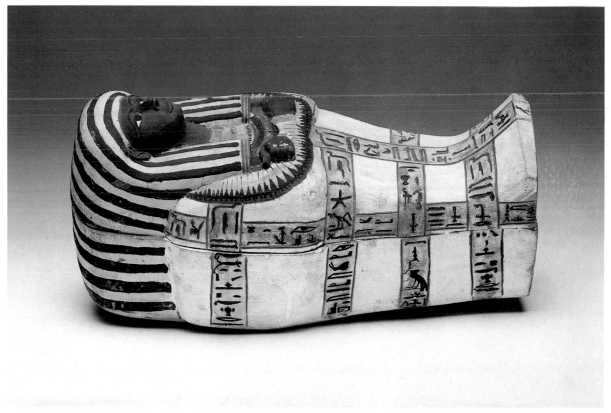

Catalogue entry number of the Cairo Museum: 27,302

Dimensions
Height (overall): 1.25 m
Length (overall: sleigh): 2.62 m
Width (overall: cornice): 0.98 m
Length of case alone: 2.07 m
Width of case alone: 0.865 m

Medium
Stuccoed wood, polychrome paint, varnish

Technique
The four panels of the case slip into the grooves of the sleigh.
    The cover is composed of two parts. This system of construction
    made it possible to place the sarcophagi containing the mummy
    on the floor of the sleigh and to assemble around it the panels
    of the case, held in place in addition by the cover.

Condition
Excellent general condition; restorations in 1975: floor consolidated;
    repasting of the scaled paint by injection

Provenance
Deir el-Medina, tomb No. 1 of Sennudjem

Date
Early in the reign of Ramses II

Bibliography
Schmidt, *Sarkofager, Mumiekister og Mumiehylster det Gamle*
    Aegypten, Copenhagen, 1919, p. 123, Fig. 628
Maspero, *Guide du visiteur du Musée du Caire*, 3rd edition,
    Cairo, 1914, p. 377, No. 3772
BIE, 2nd series, No. 7, 1886, Cairo, 1887, pp. 204-205 (who erroneously
    attributed Khons' container to lyneferty)
Daressy-toda, *ASAE* XX, 1920, pp. 151-158
Porter-Moss, Burney, I-1 (1960), p. 5, for complementary bibliography
Barguet, *Le Livre des Morts des Anciens Egyptiens*, Paris, 1967
Desroches Noblecourt, *Peintures de Temples et de Tombes*
    Égyptiens, UNESCO pocketbook, Paris, 1959-60

Desroches Noblecourt *et alii*
Catalogue of the Ramsès le Grand exhibition, Paris, 1976,
    No. XLV, pp. 194-205

Among all the civilian funerary cases discovered to date, that of Khons is unquestionably the best preserved. Its form suggests that of the ancient "Sanctuary of the South", with the roof convex at one end, placed on a large rectangular chest, the "Egyptian cornice" hanging over it. The base is made of a sort of sleigh which facilitated its towing. It corresponded to the granite sleigh of royal tombs. The marvelously preserved paintings (white background, yellowed by the aging of the varnish) show vignettes and texts excerpted from the famous Book of the Dead. Since it belonged to Khons, one of Sennudjem's sons who lived during the period of Ramses II, it is also contemporary with the great king.

While royal funerary cases from this period have, at their four angles, the image in the semi-round of the four winged goddesses who protected the dead, the latter, without wings, are represented in this civilian "version" in the center of the two small sides of the piece of furniture. Isis and Nephthys are back to back and Neith and Selket are in the same position. Nephthys is dressed in an archaic tunic adorned with V-shaped embroideries, speckled with dots, while the three other goddesses wear a similar tunic which, however, suggests a net with hexagonal links. In the centre are flowers whose heart is alternately green or black. The sheath is held by red straps with white edges. That of Nephthys is adorned with more or less large bars of various colors. Barefoot, the goddesses wear the usual jewelry—throat-pieces, bracelets, armlets and belts. The inscriptions they seem to be reading allude to the reassembling of the dismembered body of Osiris (with whom the deceased is assimilated) by Nephthys and Selket. As for Isis, she promises she will straighten the head of the deceased so that he may be reborn like a new sun while Neith will protect his embalming. On the two large sides of the funerary case is a magnificent decoration whose lower part features a funerary text—Chapter 1 of the Book of the Dead—and the upper part, magical polychrome vignettes. At each end is a spirit with an ibis head. Each turns its back to the angle of the piece of furniture; the one in the rear—the runners are considered the front of the sleigh—represents the North, the one in front, the South. With a green head, black beak, red body, having the appearance of Thoth, and wearing a divine loincloth with the characteristic belt knot, a shoulder-belt crossing the chest, these spirits of the North and South both brandish the sign of the sky on a special staff. In front of each, separated by the inscription columns, are the spirits showing the four sons of Horus. Those who are in the North, i.e. Imsety, with a man's head, and Hapy, with a baboon head, watch the bearer of the sign of the sky while those of the South, Qebsennuef, with a falcon head, and Duamutef, with the head of a young black dog, precede the bearer. They are also garbed in the divine loincloth but their torsos are covered with a bodice with two straps which imitate birds' feathers. Their hands, slightly thrust forward, imitate the attitude of those of the four goddesses.

The upper central decoration of the funerary case's left flank is adorned with vignettes on two levels. In the lower section, one first sees the mummy of the deceased, placed on a lion-headed bed on which unguent vessels have been placed. Anubis, with a young dog's head, completes the preparation of the mummy, protected by a dais whose top roughly suggests the form of that of the funerary case. The fabric covering it at mid-height is identical to that of the robes of the three goddesses and ends in a row of pompoms. On each side, Isis, in a red robe, and Nephthys, in a white robe, their arms crossed on their chests, watch over Osiris. At left, above a building with a door dominated by a cornice, and in front of a basket of bread offerings, crowned with an ample bouquet, is the image of the immaterial part of man which he finds *after* his death—a bird with human head, legs and feet. The presence of the deceased's wife, in the form of his ''bird-spirit'' with a magnificent, long wig, should be noted for the second time.

Leaving the chthonic field, one turns to the upper part. The essential motif is composed of two lions which guard the horizon, their backs to each other. Between their manes appears the horizon from which

is suspended the cross of life, giving birth to the rising sun. Khons prays in front of the one at right and the inscription above him reveals he is worshipping Re-horakhty. No one doubts that Khons hopes to reappear within this initial solar power.

Among many other details, one should be especially noted in regard to this form of Egyptian decorative art wherein an infinite variety is expressed in uniformity. The images of the two lions, apparently similar but which differ from so many standpoints, should be carefully considered. To the left of the lions, a cow wearing a *menat* necklace inscribed with the name of Hathor, with a *flabellum* standing behind its hindquarters and dominated by the *wdjat* eye, is as if mummified in a shroud, its decoration recalling that of the robes of the goddesses. The cow seems to rise out of a basin of water. Before it is placed the head of a falcon. The horizontal inscription, on either side of the cow's horns, specifies that it is the falcon of Horus who arises out of Nun, Lord of the Goddess Methyer, the Great Floating One (of the primeval waters). This is an illustration of Chapter 61 of the Book of the Dead, traced at the base of the large opposite side, i.e., the righthand panel, while the other vignettes belong to Chapter 17.

Another vignette of extreme importance of Chapter 17 is found on the right-hand panel. It concerns the papyrus shelter, this time maintained by a central column with a lyriform capital, under which the same couple is found–Khons alone, like his father, playing *senet* and his wife, Tameket, as attentive as Sennudjem's wife. Like her mother-in-law, she, too, does not participate in the action.

The decoration of this tent, the *seh*, which is much more opulent than that of Sennudjem, is complemented by a large, high bouquet framed by two large poppies. The two *wdjat* eyes dominate the *seh* and another, much larger sacred eye was traced above an image of the mummified cow. The falcon's head, visible on the upper section, has disappeared and the inscription, which dominates Khons in prayer, calls it the Mistress of the Sky.

On the upper section, on a bevelled base and a papyrus mat, two divine shapes are crouched, each holding the sign of life on their knees. The first suggests an unusual form of the dog of Anubis; the other, with a human face, cannot be identified with certainty. Is it an allusion to the spirit Qebsennuef? Next comes the representation of a chest recalling the "Sanctuary of the North" and whose proportions and decoration could suggest a *shawabti* chest with the cover separate. Finally, at right, are two versions of the spirit of the Flood–a small, standing man with a swollen torso and green flesh wearing the loincloth of the marshes and the divine beard. The two basins in which he places his hands could be an allusion to the "flow" of Osiris, confused with the annual flooding. Behind him is a more classical image of the spirit of the Flood holding the bud stems, suggesting perpetual renewal, while the eye of the falcon, located in a sort of egg which it seems to protect with one hand, would refer to the phases of the moon and the rhythm of time.

On the convex head of the cover are painted the two black dogs of Anubis facing each other, like attentive watchdogs, stretched out on a white *naos*, the *flabellum* dominating their hindquarters. Around their necks, they wear the traditional necklaces and scarves. In the centre is the animated sign of the West where the dead are buried.

On the other side, one sees the goddess Nut, the "Great, Mother of the god", "Mistress of the Sky". Her winged arms are outstretched. The goddess' skin is green, her robe with two straps leaving her chest bare is red. A long white belt, twice wrapped around her waist, recalls those of Isis and Nephthys protecting the mummy. The remainder of the roof of this funerary case is crossed by wrappings arranged in a manner similar to that of the wrappings around the shroud. In the areas thus provided are several spirits, including the four sons of Horus–Hapy, Imsety, Duamutef and Qebsennuef–and, twice, the couple Kohns and Tamaket, sumptuously dressed, the first with one knee on the ground and the second, fully kneeling.

Once again, on a monument used by only *one* deceased person, the latter is shown, accompanied by his wife. Her role is to surround him with her urgent attentions or to stand by his side, vigilant, as in the group of bird-spirits. Undoubtedly, this is a discreet allusion to the essential role women had to perform for their deceased husbands with a view to rebirth in the world of eternity.

On each side of the cover, fitting in the free space, a magnificent upright cobra extends the coils of its body which tapers to the tip of its tail.

Bibliography
(cf. *Nota bene* at the bottom of the technical description of object
40.)

The "funerary furniture" of civilians sometimes contained imitations of precious vases, sculpted in wood.
This imitation, pear-shaped vessel with a flat bottom,
a low belly and a short neck ending in a flared lip was
placed in the tomb of Sennudjem. On the stuccoed
sides, the white paint of the background is veined to
imitate alabaster. In the centre, a line of hieroglyphs
traced in black on a yellow background tells us that the
object belonged to "the Osiris Servant of the Master of
the Two Lands, Sennudjem".

The small flat stopper, placed on the protruding
rim, bears, as is often the case, a charming decoration
in bright colors copying the heart of a lotus viewed
from the top of the flower.

Khabekhnet *shawabti* chest

Catalogue entry number of the Cairo Museum: J.27,296

Dimensions
Height: 0.30 m

Medium
Stuccoed and painted wood

Technique
Composed of several pieces of wood; fastening with tenons, mortises and pegs; removable cover

Condition
Scaled color in some places on the sleigh and at the top of the uprights

Provenance
Deir el-Medina

Date
19th dynasty

Bibliography
(cf. *Nota bene* at the bottom of the technical description of object 40.)

This small chest in the form of the archaic Sanctuary of the North, placed on a sleigh, contained a portion of the funerary figurines, or *shawabtis*, of one of the sons of Sennudjem, Khabekhnet.

The small sleigh which, in principle, was used to more easily move the box laden down with its contents, is painted red. On the latter is fastened the high, rectangular cabinet whose lateral uprights dominate the horizontal top. The uprights are used to help keep the cover convex. The cabinet was closed with a small cord connecting two yellow buttons, one on the top of the cover, the other on the upper part of the chest. The two ends of the small cord were then fastened in a terracotta seal–the classic manner of closing doors, boxes, chests and cabinets in Egypt.

The decoration is fully geometric. It is composed as if one had wished to imitate three doors integrated in one another, made of light green, upside-down, U-shaped bands which stand out against a blue-green background. The top of the cover has two curved ribbons of the same color and the same background. The outline of the bands is wavy while in the centre of the motifs, a vertical yellow area, regularly defined, contains a vertical column of inscriptions in black hieroglyphs framed by two red lines. It reads: "The blessed with Osiris, Khabekhnet, the justified".

● *Shawabtis*

Shawabtis were the name given by the Egyptians to small figurines bearing the likeness of the mummified deceased, placed in tombs among the objects of ritual funerary furniture. This type appeared in the Middle Kingdom. The tombs in which they are discovered generally have only one *shawabti*, often rather primitive, made of clay or wood, and sometimes placed in a miniature sarcophagus. The name comes directly from the word *shawab*, a variety of tree from which the first *shawabtis* were thought to have been carved.

In the New Kingdom, a limited number of *shawabtis* continue to be found in burial vaults. Sennefer, the mayor of Thebes under Amenophis II, seems to have had only two of them. However, they quickly grew in number; the richest tombs had hundreds of them of highly varied quality (cf. tomb of Tutankhamun); in fact, it was claimed there was one for each day of the year. But this hypothesis has not yet been fully confirmed. In the 19th dynasty, some *shawabtis* no longer were wrapped in a shroud but could, in some cases, wear the festive costume of the living. They were supposed to represent the foremen who supervised workers. The inscription, which, beginning in this period, is engraved in horizontal lines from the pelvis to the ankles of the figurine, reproduced the text of Chapter 6 of the Book of the Dead wherein the statuette is asked to carry out the work to be demanded of its owner in the other world.

Chapter 6 of the Book of the Dead reads: "O thou *shawabti* of X, if I am called upon, if I am designated to do all the work usually done in the kingdom of the dead, lo, obstacles have been set up for him yonder as a man to his duties, thou art charged with all these tasks that are wont to be done yonder, to cultivate the fields, to irrigate the shores, to transport sand of the East to the West. 'Here I am!' shalt thou say."

Starting in the 21st dynasty, the figurine took the name of *ushabti*, composed of the verb *ushab*, "to answer", thereby moving closer to the servant role assigned the object.

Generally, the statuette wore a necklace which may be seen on the shroud. Both hands were crossed on the chest. Like Osiris' hand, each usually holds two hoes for the agricultural labor to be done.

In back, on the shoulder, was usually a sack of grain or vessels to carry water, suspended from a yoke. In the beginning, miniature models of these accessories were placed next to the figurines.

Catalogue entry number of the Cairo Museum: J.27,232

Dimensions
Height: 0.19 m

Medium
Limestone

Technique
Made in one piece

Condition
Good; scratches on the nose, the right cheek and the chin

Provenance
Deir el-Medina

Date
19th dynasty

Bibliography
(cf. *Nota bene* at the bottom of the technical description of object
    40.)

For *shawabtis* in general:
Aubert, *Statuettes égyptiennes, chaouabtis, oushebtis*, Paris, 1974
Schneider, *Shabtis I, II, III*, Rapenburg, 1977

This *shawabti* represents the scribe Ramose who
seemingly was in charge of two crews of workers
laboring in the royal hypogea under Ramses II. This, at
least, is what the inscription traced on a horizontal
strip implies.
      Ramose's face is painted dark red, illuminated by
two big eyes with black and white details. The wig,
covering three-quarters of the ears, has long, cascad-
ing curls. This detail, like the bare feet visible under
the sheath, suggests the costume of the "living"
rather than a true shroud. The headband adorning the
head is restricted at the top by a ribbon painted red
and opening out in the middle of the forehead in a blue
lotus, its red stem passing over the top of the skull. A
broad collar is also indicated by red lines on a yellow
background. The two hands, which are dark ochre,
hold two yellow hoes, outlined in red.

Catalogue entry number of the Cairo Museum: 27,251

Dimensions
Height: 0.29 m

Medium
Limestone

Technique
In a single piece

Condition
Good

Provenance
Deir el-Medina

Date
19th dynasty

Bibliography
(cf. *Nota bene* at the bottom of the technical description of object
    40.)

This *shawabti* image belonging to Sennudjem is
extremely classical in form. The face, rather thin, is
painted dark red, with details highlighted in black,
mainly on the eyes. The dark, blue-green wig is also
the most commonly found on *shawabtis*, showing the
ears. Its body, in an Osirian attitude, is wrapped in a
white shroud. The hands, crossed on the chest, hold
two hoes painted red. The floral details of the large
collar do not extend to the shoulders.
    On the lower part of the body is Chapter 6 of the
Book of the Dead on eight horizontal lines of black
hieroglyphs separated by thin red lines. Under the
shroud, the sculptor indicates the location of the feet
with two veins in relief.

● Toiletries–accessories of the living and the dead

All the objects presented here to evoke the daily life of craftsmen of the royal necropolis and the preparation for immortality were *strictly funerary* in purpose.

It is quite obvious that the candidate for eternity, in order to blaze his trail through obstacles–the course was marked by demons–had to have the utensils necessary for his defence. The visitor has just seen the *senet* game (cf. 46), which certainly was used by the living for recreation but which was also essential to pass *post-mortem* trials. A similar phenomenon is noted regarding the headrest (cf. 40) and the blue bowl (cf. 41). With ample evidence to support the theory, it may be stated that, in addition to essentially funerary objects such as sarcophagi, *shawabtis*, amulets, heart-shaped scarabs and all the jewelry of the deceased, the other objects found in burial vaults, while for the most part commonly used in daily life, were placed at the disposal of the deceased as instruments of protection.

Mirror

Catalogue entry number of the Cairo Museum: 10,888

Dimensions
Height: 0.305 m

Medium
Bronze

Technique
The disk is inserted in the handle through its tenon which thus penetrates into the centre of the umbel of the papyrus. Fastening completed by a rivet.

Condition
Good

Provenance
Saqqara (1860)

Date
New Kingdom (18th dynasty)

Bibliography
(cf. *Nota bene* at the bottom of the technical description of object 40.)
Husson, *L'offrande du miroir dans les temples égyptiens de l'époque gréco-romaine*, Lyon, 1977

This mirror is composed of a rounded bronze surface, slightly flattened at the top and base. In Antiquity, it was obviously polished until it could be used effectively to reflect an undeformed, sufficiently clear image. Its handle is made of a young, nude woman with a long wig, a high, slender waist and arms hanging along the body. A papyrus head whose lower part is integrated with the top of the wig falls in an elegant curve.

The mirror, which, naturally, was frequently used by the living, could be carried in a small pouch with handles or placed in a precious chest taking the general form of the object.

Humble women looked at their reflections in the water, texts reveal. Middle-class women and ladies had mirrors in the shape of copper disks, sometimes gold- or silver-plated. From the early period, the handle was generally a stem or a papyrus umbel, but there were also variants in the form of shields. In the New Kingdom, fantasy, forever guided by strictly observed symbolism, allowed a wider variety of handle shapes. Sometimes, one sees images of divinities associated with the Legend of the Far-Off Goddess, the god Bes, related to births (cf. headrest, 40), signs of protection (the *sa* sign and the *djed* pillar), the figure of the goddess Hathor, bouquets of flowers replacing the strands of the papyrus umbel, adorned with small falcons balanced on the umbel and small, palm-shaped or lotus-shaped pillars. However, most of the time, the essential themes were papyrus and the goddess Hathor. In these cases, the handle showed either the head of the goddess with cows' ears dominated by the papyrus umbel, or the body of a nude woman, suggesting Hathor, crowned with the same umbel. As for the entire series of so-called "toilet" articles, the mirror "of the living" had considerable religious significance and, naturally, a posthumous role. On the walls of Ptolemaic temples, the offering of two gold and silver mirrors clearly proves they were used to ensure eternal life, suggested by the symbols of the sun and the moon bringing about the perpetual renewal of cosmic movement. The deceased was thus helped to reach immortality.

54

Razor

Catalogue entry number of the Cairo Museum: 63,686

Dimensions
Length: 0.166 m

Medium
Bronze and wood

Technique
The wooden handle is fastened to the bronze blade with rivets.

Condition
Very good

Provenance
Deir el-Medina

Date
New Kingdom

Bibliography
(cf. *Nota bene* at the bottom of the technical description of object
    40.)

This bronze razor has a form typical of the New Kingdom. Beginning with the time of the pyramids, included in "funerary furniture" among objects intended for the toilet of the deceased, were small, rectangular blades measuring between five and seven centimetres, remotely suggesting the blades of the former mechanical razors, though slightly larger. In addition, their central surface is a few millimetres thick to facilitate gripping. The four sides become slimmer, forming sharp edges. Some were made of silex. The mother of Kheops, Hetepheres, received one made of gold—it was therefore votive. In the 6th dynasty, the wife of the vizier Izi at Edfu had identically shaped copper razors, kept in a small wooden chest; others were represented on the walls of sanctuaries of Old Kingdom tombs.

The advanced version used in the New Kingdom reflects real progress in the use of the instrument whose various contours conform to the surfaces to be shaved. This type of razor was later used by the Carthaginians.

Among the more than 2,000 objects contained in Tutankhamun's funerary treasure was a box with a receptacle in the shape of this object. The inscription indicated it was the razor of "His Majesty when he was a child". It is quite obvious that the instrument was not used for a beard since he had none yet. However, there was a tradition that a heavy lock of hair be kept on the right side of the skull of young princes. The rest of the hair was shaved.

If it is assumed that the objects in the funerary treasure of the deceased, most of which were used by the living, were placed in burial vaults to assist in the transformation of the dead, the razors must then be categorized among the series of instruments which suggest childhood—a symbol of the phase of resurrection of the young sun.

Rake-comb

Catalogue entry number of the Cairo Museum: 36,233

Dimensions
Height: 0.055 m
Length: 0.17 m

Medium
Wood

Technique
Incised floral decoration, formerly inlaid with colored pastes

Condition
Good

Provenance
Abusir el-Melek

Date
New Kingdom, 19th dynasty

Bibliography
(cf. *Nota bene* at the bottom of the technical description of object 40.)

The combs used by the Egyptians may be single or double and, in the latter case, they naturally have finer teeth on one side than on the other. They are generally rectangular in form with relatively straight sides which are rather flat. They are preferably sculpted in a hard wood. The most luxurious have teeth on one side only. On the other side—i.e., at the top of the object—a plant or animal decoration adorns the object and serves as a handle. One of the most elegant is dominated by the image of a Nubian ibex, its front legs folded on the ground (Louvre).

It would appear these small combs were used more frequently to comb natural hair than the very elaborate wigs of the New Kingdom. The latter required special instruments—long pins, small tongs adorned with animals or figures on one of the two elements which made them up.

The upper part of the comb exhibited here, which was used to hold it, is decorated with a regular frieze of lotus petals and was formerly inlaid with colored pigments. At the top, four small protuberances complete the decoration.

Miniature chest

Catalogue entry number of the Cairo Museum: 3,318

Dimensions
Height: 0.078 m

Medium
Wood and ivory

Technique
All parts assembled with wooden pegs

Condition
Good

Provenance
Gourna

Bibliography
(cf. *Nota bene* at the bottom of the technical description of object 40.)

This small box resembles a miniature version of the large storage chests with desk-shaped covers, sometimes used as chests by scribes to hold their fresh rolls of papyrus. (The book or document rolls were placed in long terracotta cases whose covers pivoted on a peg which sometimes bore the title of the writing.)

The small chest exhibited among the deceased's "toiletries" may perhaps have contained tiny unguent jars. It might just as well have been better used for jewels or for material to seal anything to be protected from theft or premature opening—cylinders to print the top of the pointed terracotta stoppers of wine jars or to mark the sealing of certain official documents—scarabs affixed to small sigillary surfaces of clay which linked the threads hanging from the buttons of the cover and the top of the vessel.

Here, the body of the box resembles a miniature temple, the uprights ending in legs which allow air to circulate under the object. The top of the box is dominated by the classical "Egyptian cornice", suggesting the opening of palm leaves. Its decoration is inlaid with small ivory plates.

Catalogue entry number of the Cairo Museum: 25,226

Dimensions
Length: 0.115 m

Medium
Schist

Technique
Sculpted in a single piece

Condition
Very good

Date
New Kingdom

Bibliography
(cf. *Nota bene* at the bottom of the technical description of object
      40.)
(cf. bibliography of the blue bowl, 41, *in fine*).

Whether this small vessel was used to contain the unguents of an Egyptian lady or was only placed in a tomb to provide the deceased with the perfumed grease needed to reconstitute the flesh, it was sculpted in the likeness of a protective animal. Here, the animal is an *inet* fish, known by the common name of *bulti*, which suggests one of the transformations the dead had to undergo for happy rebirth (cf. glazed floor-tile, 18). The fish portrayed here is a *tilapia nilotica*, recognizable by its line and the slight swelling of its body. The characteristic tail and fins are ribbed, the mandibles straight, the head marked by a large, round eye while the body is without scales but is covered with overlapping lines imitating the small waves of water which Egyptian artists always drew vertically to show an aquatic surface. The object must therefore be set upright with the head on top, showing the fish virtually bursting from the wave. Simultaneously, the spirit of the deceased it represents comes to the surface. This very fact illuminates the position of the fish-shaped glass vessel (British Museum, London) from Tell el-Amarna which, to be used and to facilitate comprehension, had to be set upright, on the tail. A lotus flower, naturally, could be placed on the vessel, recalling the sun lotus which the small fish bore in its mandibles as it emerged from its aquatic peregrinations.

Shell- and duck-shaped receptacle

Catalogue entry number of the Cairo Museum: 30,759

Dimensions
Length: 0.143 m

Medium
Alabaster

Technique
Great elegance in treatment

Condition
Very good

Provenance
Thebes West (?)

Date
New Kingdom

Bibliography
(cf. *Nota bene* at the bottom of the technical description of object 40.)

The object resembles the bowl of a spoon but it is undoubtedly a bowl designed to contain unguents. The bowls of spoons sculpted in alabaster–a duck's neck and head were placed on one side–have been found in princely tombs of the New Kingdom (in the tomb of Tuya, Ramses' mother, for example).

The twisted neck and beak of the duck serve as a handle for the receptacle. The duck is a wild marsh bird whose harmful effect had to be neutralized since, in the primeval waters, it was likely to disturb the progress of the seed of the deceased as it was being reconstituted (cf. 17). The neck was twisted by the boomerang of an invisible hunter who, on his skiff, exterminated the animal which symbolized evil spirits. The contents of the bowl of the spoon, in the form of a shell, were thereby protected and the unguents would not become rancid, spared, as they were, from decomposition.

Unguent "spoon"
with decorated handle

Catalogue entry number of the Cairo Museum: 49,540

Dimensions
Height: 0.215 m

Medium
Wood

Technique
Decoration in relief sculpted on a wooden board

Condition
Quite good. Polychromy gone

Provenance
Saqqara (1925)

Date
End of the New Kingdom (?)

Bibliography
(cf. *Nota bene* at the bottom of the technical description of object
    40.)
Desroches Noblecourt, *Un lac de turquoise*, in Monuments et
    Mémoires PIOT, XLVII, Paris, 1953, pp. 1-34

The only unguent bowl whose general appearance suggests the bowl of a spoon is the object exhibited here. On the upper part is a rounded receptacle; a bucolic scene sculpted on the bottom in the form of a board may have served as a handle. It is nevertheless a bowl designed to hold fragrant grease and made "operative" by a vivid context.

At the top forming the receptacle is a pool suggested by the zigzagged water line which completely encircles it. At the two upper corners, lotuses recall the birth of the sun, which was supposed to emerge from their calyx. Two papyrus heads appear on the base.

Under the pool is shown what should, in reality, have formed the landscape of the body of water, i.e., a marsh from which springs a stylized papyrus screen with three flowers and four buds on long stems. At the base, the very characteristic leaflets of these aquatic plants are represented by a series of triangles filled with veins which may been seen at the base of all the papyrus-shaped columns of Egyptian monuments. Immediately above, on the surface of the water, a barque with the prow and stern retracted, adorned with papyrus heads, glides forward through the labor of two nude bargemen, each wielding a long pole. According to the classical custom, the movement runs from left to right. In the centre of the barque is a small prone calf. This is the common representation, known since the time of the pyramids and often found in paintings in burial vaults of the 19th dynasty, of the rising sun—the "suckling calf". It is the deceased one hopes will be reborn with the new sun in the world of eternity. Such an image further reinforced the effectiveness of the unguents in the "spoon".

60

Female swimmer formerly holding a duck(?)-shaped box

Catalogue entry number of the Cairo Museum: 5,218

Dimensions
Length: 0.34 m

Medium
Wood

Technique
The head and neck are set in and fastened with a tenon at shoulder
height. Two other tenons, still visible, were driven in under the
body of the duck (?) which the woman held and which has disappeared.

Provenance
Herber Collection

Date
Late in the 18th dynasty

Bibliography
(cf. *Nota bene* at the bottom of the technical description of object
40.)

The most elaborate and poetic shape given this type of
cosmetic bowl is that of the so-called "female swimmer" type. Some museums have objects of the same
genre in their collections. The only real variant is the
headdress of the female swimmer.
      The craftsman used all the resources of his imagi-
nation to give protective power to the bowl to be
placed in a tomb. The bowl contained unguents to
reconstitute the flesh of the mummy. This elegant version is made up of a young woman floating on the
water with her body stretched out and who lets herself
be pulled by a large marsh duck which is a prisoner in
her hands. On the object exhibited here, the bird has
disappeared, but it is no longer the wild duck whose
neck was twisted by the mortal boomerang. It is, in
fact, the same bird swimming but it is kept in the
desired direction and cannot escape. Its body is gener-

ally hollow, forming the container. The wings make up
the two parts on the cover, which could pivot on small
pegs. The young, nude woman's only jewelry is a belt
on her hips and bracelets; the sole trace is preserved
on the stucco. Decorative bars are still visible on the
back and front of the torso, as is a wide necklace. The
extremely thin face is framed by a wig with superim-

posed locks which form genuine wings on each side of
the cheeks. At right is a large lock of hair and, around
the skull, a wide headband with traces of stucco, indicating it was decorated with a floral design.

● Eye makeup

From the beginning of recorded history and probably even before the 1st dynasty, the Egyptians wore small jewels–protective amulets–and used unguents for the body and pigments for the eyes.

Logically, what was initially considered protection was quickly adapted to decorative purposes. Of all makeup, the most important was used to bring out the vividness of the gaze as well as to preserve sight against ophthalmia and conjunctivitis which were so frequent in hot countries due to sandstorms.

From early on, dark grey-black kohl, an extract of galena, and malachite powder were used to outline the eyelids. Only the use of kohl was generally preserved, especially for Pharaoh, but also for his subjects. Women in Egypt still commonly use kohl. Hundreds of underground lead sulphite mine galleries were discovered recently at Gebel Zeit, three kilometres from the Red Sea in Upper Egypt. The mines provided pharaohs with kohl for more than a thousand years and perhaps even from the beginning of the dynasties.

For the Egyptians, it was the eyes which introduced life and the personality of the subject most intensively into statuary, reliefs and paintings. As much as possible, they sought to inlay the eyes in images of the gods and the more carefully executed images of men. In painting and drawing, the gaze could not be atrophied under any circumstances. For this reason, the eyes were always shown from a front view.

Once one entered the supernatural world of the gods and the dead, the eyes became those of the celestial gaze, the sun and the moon. It was therefore essential that their integrity be carefully preserved. (Divine legends allude to the wounded eye of the god which must be recovered in good condition–the moon).

In the temple of Kôm Ombo, for example, amid religious inscriptions and representations, an entire panel is reserved, from top to bottom, for the very detailed nomenclature of the kit of an oculist. If needed, it would be used to care for the eye of the god which might have been attacked!

In the same context but applied to the simple mortal, the presence of containers for kohl or galena introduced into the accessories of the dead allowed the gaze on eternity, solar or lunar, to be preserved, if need be. In tombs, triple bowls were sometimes placed with three different types of makeup, manufactured under the supervision of physicians and intended to protect the eyes during the three seasons of the year.

Kohl pot

Catalogue entry number of the Cairo Museum: 30,776

Dimensions
Height: 0.047 m

Medium
Dark turquoise blue glazed terracotta

Technique
Cover added

Condition
Very good

Provenance
Abydos

Date
Late 18th dynasty (?)

Bibliography
(cf. *Nota bene* at the bottom of the technical description of object
40.)

This small pot takes the classical form of small kohl containers, as have been found in tombs, still containing galena powder preserved in a small piece of linen bound under the lip of the object and protected by a small flat stopper. One or two stylets were often placed next to the pot to allow its contents to be used. Generally, the pot was made of alabaster. Like this one, it could also be made of glazed terracotta covered with tones of color varying from light turquoise, frequently turned pale green, to dark turquoise or even indigo at the end of the 18th dynasty.

The belly of the pot is decorated with drawings traced in black and suggesting a blossoming lotus flower. The base of the petals is also flecked with small black dots. It is from the lotus that the rising sun emerged; one of the eyes of the dead was sometimes assimilated with it.

Kohl pot with monkey

Catalogue entry number of the Cairo Museum: 31,244

Dimensions
Height: 0.05 m

Medium
Dark turquoise blue glazed terracotta; black decoration

Technique
Made of a single piece

Condition
The stopper is missing.

Provenance
Kaw (?)

Date
Late 18th dynasty (?)

Bibliography
(cf. *Nota bene* at the bottom of the technical description of object 40.)

This kohl pot bears a touch of fantasy which presided over the manufacture of small makeup containers in the New Kingdom. Breaking with the monotony of the simple container, the craftsman fashioned it by giving it a cylindrical shape, successfully completed by the silhouette of a kneeling cercopithecus monkey which both presents and maintains it. The likeness of one of the familiar animals that helped enhance the recreation of Nile dwellers was thus introduced into the decoration.

Two small holes on each side mark the location of the fastening rings of the cover.

Double-necked makeup pot

Catalogue entry number of the Cairo Museum: 72,178

Dimensions
Height: 0.13 m

Medium
Glazed turquoise blue terracotta

Technique
Made of a single piece

Condition
Peeling at the top of the right neck

Provenance
Abydos

Date
New Kingdom, 19th dynasty (?)

Bibliography
(cf. *Nota bene* at the bottom of the technical description of object 40.)

Another version of the makeup pot is that which was paired with two to four other pots to contain different products. Here, the small pot is designed to hold two types of pigment for the eyes. The belly of the object suggests two cylinders standing side by side in a wrapping, though the tops of the cylinders are left free. The edges of the latter are bounded by a black line. The case is decorated at the top and at the base with a frieze of lotus petals drawn in black and bordered with lines which are also black. In the centre, on the full height, a small, apparently nude woman is drawn with one arm folded on her chest holding an unidentified object (a flower?). Her other arm hangs beside her body. Her hand grasps a lotus bud with a curved stem.

Ramses' destiny

Two refined ritual statuettes bearing the likeness of the sovereign and the episodes of his coronation and confirming the power which marked his reign are installed here to introduce the next to last module with the cover of the mummy-shaped sarcophagus in which Ramses was reentombed.

Throughout the exhibition, the visitor has been in contact with the great sovereign. He was welcomed by Ramses' colossal effigies and the evocation of his majestic, indeed gigantic, temples. In sometimes strange ways, the king sought to broach the mentalities of his time so as to better promote innovative concepts and to make them more compatible with religion. The "royal propaganda" is also better perceived when one literally comes into contact with the immediate ancestors of the king. Next, thanks to artistic evidence recalling the fields of science and letters, the focus was placed on various manifestations of the civilization of the period. The visitor thus penetrated further into Ramses' intimacy, becoming aware of the pomp of the palace and the elegance and beauty of the great ladies who are so present and so close to us.

When, on the first floor, the visitor entered the domain of the craftsmen who labored for the king, he will have realized that such men had not forgotten to prepare the ritual furniture which would enable them, too, to cross the long "purgatory" which, after a "pre-christic" judgment, would lead them to the Great All.

After such an extensive overview, one must come back to the sovereign himself. As great, as powerful as he was, he is nonetheless shown—ritually—crawling on the branches of the *ished* tree. It is strewn with fruit bearing his coronation name to further guarantee the eternity of his reign. Opposite, the sphinx, with the idealized face of the king, ensures, by its very presence, the monarch's perpetual solar reappearance on the horizon.

With another face—this one assumed—Ramses appears at the end of his earthly existence. His tomb having been looted, the priests of the 21st dynasty saved his remains just in time and buried them again in the sarcophagus of one of his close predecessors while renewing his rites of preservation. He had been robbed of all his jewels and all his sumptuous sarcophagi. A small papyrus was simply slipped around his neck to protect that vulnerable part of his body while on his chest were placed new garlands of fresh flowers. The sarcophagus is exhibited vertically, as it never was inside the rock-cut tomb where Ramses lay in his successive wrappings, placed horizontally on a funerary bed, awaiting his resurrection. The last day of the funeral, everything changed when those who surrounded the "great voyager" on his departure towards the Life of Eternity placed the mummy of his final anthropoid coffin before the entrance to the tomb.

Then began the ceremonies of "the Opening of the Mouth and Eyes" to return to the deceased the use of all his senses as he started on the road towards immortality. The great material trials the king had to undergo before being twice saved by the priests of the 21st dynasty are now a matter of record.

The funerary wrapping is presented here in keeping with the ritual which Merenptah—Ramses' 13th son and successor—carried out before the tomb, dressed in a feline skin.

Catalogue entry number of the Cairo Museum: 37,423
General Cairo catalogue: 42,142

Dimensions
Height: 0.275 m
Total length (restoration of the base included): 0.758 m
Maximum width (base): 0.125 m
Length without restoration: 0.64 m

Medium
Greenish grey schist

Technique
Monolithic sculpture in the round, extremely well-executed and of
great beauty. Only the object placed on the altar was added.
Text, branches, leaves and offerings shown in intaglio engraved
lines.

Condition
The piece has been mutilated; missing are the front of the base and
part of the offering table; the entire left front angle of the altar
(restored) and the object attached to the tray of the altar; the
rear part of the base and the right leg (restored). Cracks in the
arms and the left foot; plaster connections on the left arm and
near the left shoulder; traces of wear on the right side and on
the tail of the *uraeus;* numerous but slight scratches and scores
over the whole object. Traces of a whitish deposit, particularly
in the hollow of the hieroglyphic signs.

Provenance
Eastern Thebes, Temple of Karnak, *cachette* in the courtyard between
the hypostyle hall and the seventh pylon; found May 7, 1904

Date
Time of Ramses II

Bibliography
For the discovery, cf.
Legrain, *Les récentes découvertes de Karnak, BIE*, 4th series,
No. 5, 1904, pp. 109-119; *id.* No. 6, 1905, pp. 109-128

For the statuette of Ramses II and for comparison with similar sculp-
tures, cf.
Legrain, *Statues*, II, 1909, pp. 7-8, No. 42142, Pl. IV; *id.* pp. 8-9,
pls. V and VI
Newberry, *Rekhmara*, Pl. XXII
Matthiew, *JEA*, XVI, 1930, pp. 31-32, Pl. XI
Aldred, *JEA*, Vol. 41, 1955, pp. 3-8, Pl. I
Helck, *ZÄS* 82, 1957, p. 127 (inscriptions)

For general technical considerations, cf.
Müller, *Der Torso einer Königsstatue . . .*,
Studi in memoria di Ippolito Rosellini, Vol. II,
Pisa, 1955, Pl. XVIII and p. 187 and ff.
Zeinab el Kordy, *Présentation des feuilles des arbres Ished Im et
Baq, ASAE*, LXIX, 1983, pp. 268-286
This sculpture is reproduced in numerous general works listed in
Porter-Moss, Burney, II (1972), pp. 141-142

Desroches Noblecourt *et alii*
Catalogue of the Ramsès le Grand exhibition, Paris, 1976,
No. XLIX, pp. 232-237

This magnificent work in schist shows Ramses during a religious ceremony, stripped to the waist, wearing a loincloth which is archaic but pleated and free-falling in the back in keeping with the fashion of the time. He wears the royal headcloth, the *nemes*. The representation is that of a moment in the ritual when Pharaoh, kneeling first on one knee, then the other, the torso almost horizontal, the rear leg straight, presents to his god, in an infinitely respectful posture, a sort of box dominated by a cornice on which his name may have been written in a rebus. Possibly, a ram's head of Amun was shown. The box was used as a cover for the sacred vessel in which the first water of the flood was to be drawn. In front of the base is a small table of offerings in flat relief. This royal stance is found from the beginning of the 18th dynasty. Amenophis IV himself did not deviate from it when he worshipped Aten.

The rite evoked here was carried out upon the arrival of the flood.

An even more important detail is to be considered: the branches with rather pointed leaves and the fruit on which the king crawls. The role played by the famous *ished* tree, the *mimusops Schimperi Hochst*, is known. It was the sacred tree which had grown in the courtyard of the great sun temple of Heliopolis where royal coronation festivities were celebrated. Myth had it that Seshat, goddess of the Annals, wrote the new name of Pharaoh with her reed pen the day Pharaoh was crowned and proclaimed sovereign. Several representations on the walls of temples illustrate the ceremonial act at Karnak or at the Ramesseum, the king's jubilee temple. The new sovereign is seated, his back turned to Amun-Re-Atum.

The former traced the name Usimaare-Setepenre on a fruit, surrounded by numerous small leaves. Opposite, standing, Sechat, protectress of libraries, also writes the coronation name, her reed pen halted at the sign of the sun.

The millions of years of jubilees wished for the king were certainly not as numerous on earth as the hope the monument expressed but it is known that Ramses is one of the sovereigns who remained longest on the throne; this notion of renewal was to perpetuate itself beyond death. (The partially destroyed inscription engraved around the base, mentioning the *ished* tree gives the protocol of the pharaoh, made up of his five names as well as some epithets.)

Among the miniature works from the Ramses era, this sculpture is one of the most harmonious as well as one of the most accurate. While the sovereign sacrificed monumentality, he knew how to inspire the sculptors; they literally sculpted in schist his slender, muscular body and his face which so closely approximates reality. The profile of the beardless monarch is found on the magnificent statue of Turin and in the most beautiful reliefs of Ramses' temples. Such a portrait does not distort the still almost archaic treatment of the eyes which proves to be the closest to its model.

65

Ramses as a sphinx, offering the vessel of Amun

Catalogue entry number of the Cairo Museum: 38,060
General Cairo catalogue: 42,146

Dimensions
Height: 0.18 m
Length: 0.37 m
Width: 0.09 m

Medium
Initially painted crystalline sandstone

Technique
Carefully executed. Wiry animal body, softness of the human face

Condition
Good, but broken at the right thigh and at the front of the base

Provenance
Western Thebes, Temple of Karnak, *cachette*

Bibliography
Legrain, Statues II in Catalogue général . . . du Musée du Caire,
    pp. 11-12, Pl. VIII
Helck, *Nilhöhe und Jubiläumsfest* in *ZÄS* 93, 1966, p. 74
Schott, *Die heilige Vase des Amon* in *ZÄS* 98, 1970, p. 42 and ff.
Traunecker, *Les rites de l'eau à Karnak* in *BIFAO* 72, 1972,
    p. 203 and ff.

Desroches Noblecourt *et alii*
Catalogue of the Ramsès le Grand exhibition, Paris, 1976,
    No. L, pp. 238-241

Another miniature statuette–this one sculpted in crystalline sandstone–shows the king as a sphinx, offering the famous vessel of Amun on New Year's Day, his two outstretched hands holding the belly of the vessel. As the texts abundantly state and as we have already noted, the return of the flood in Egypt coincided with the beginning of the year. The new water had to be drawn in a milennial rite perpetuated much later by the priests of Isis in the sanctuaries of Italy.

According to the inscriptions, the vessels could be made of silver, gold or copper. This one, given the fact there was initially a stucco covering, may have been gilded.

The sphinx, in all periods, was the symbol of the sun which appears on the horizon and, accordingly, of the dead king who was to awaken to eternal life. It is therefore not surprising that Ramses, for this renewal of the year corresponding to the reappearance of the rejuvenated king, wears the funerary headcloth adopted by kings on that occasion. Pharaoh nonetheless wears his large civilian ceremonial beard.

Beginning in the New Kingdom, the miniature sphinx was treated as an object of offering. That is why, in his arms, he holds the object presented to the divine effigies.

Female sphinxes, or sphinges, also began to appear in representations towards the end of the 18th dynasty, perhaps under Asiatic influence.

66

Cover of the sarcophagus in which Ramses was reentombed

Catalogue entry number of the Cairo Museum: 26,214
General Cairo catalogue: 61,020

Dimensions
Height: 2.06 m
Width at the elbows: 0.545 m
Width of the feet: 0.435 m
Depth of the feet: 0.365 m

Medium
Painted wood

Technique
Use of wood tenons, mortises and pegs. Repairs made in the 21st
    dynasty

Condition
All the precious coating has been removed along with the accessories
    decorated with inlays (serpent, scepters and beard).

Provenance
Western Thebes, royal *cachette* of Deir el-Bahri

Dates
Sarcophagus dated, based on the style, to the end of the 18th
    dynasty; the three records make it possible to date the reburials
    to *circa* 1090 BC and *circa* 970 BC

Bibliography
Porter-Moss I-1, p. 393, No. 320
Porter-Moss I-2, p. 661, 19
Maspero, *Momies royales*, pp. 556-560
Daressy, *Cercueils des cachettes royales*, Catalogue général . . . du
    Musée du Caire, pp. 32-34, Pl. XX-XXII
Černý, *JEA* 32 (1946), pp. 24-30
Thomas, *The Royal Necropolis of Thebes* (1966); p. 249, 2 b; p. 252,
    28, pp. 252-253, 29
Kitchen, *The Third Intermediate Period (1973)*, p. 417 and p. 423

Desroches Noblecourt *et alii*
Catalogue of the Ramsès le Grand exhibition, Paris, 1976,
    No. LXXII, pp. 316-323

The only royal funerary treasure of the New Kingdom preserved to date is that of Tutankhamun, the very young sovereign almost ignored by History until his tomb was discovered. The rooms in which the little sovereign was placed, surrounded by his funerary furniture, were so small they almost seem to be a store-room. However, examining this extraordinary treasure, one may imagine the splendors, the shimmer of gold with which the great Ramses must have been surrounded at the end of the 67th year of his reign. But nothing—not even, apparently, his final wrapping—has survived. The priests who reentombed the poor mummy, its wrappings almost entirely ripped away by those who had savagely stolen the jewels, undoubtedly judged the vestiges of the sarcophagi could no longer be reused. Among the coffins naturally deprived of their gold covering, found in the looted tombs of the Valley of the Kings, they chose the one which was best adapted to the remains of Ramses, hastily wrapped in a new shroud. The face of the cover recalls the features of one of the last pharaohs of the 18th dynasty, Haremhab, or Ramses I. The features are magnificent, but there is a difference in the treatment of the serpent, erect on the forehead, and the two sceptres, more or less well executed, held in the hand of the king. They were certainly added in the 21st dynasty, at the time of reburial. The visible pierced ears (cf. earrings of Sethos II, 24) should be noted.

The initial decoration has disappeared from the surface; the wood is now bare, but the veins give it a strange life, despite the vestiges of yellow paint with which it was covered along with some black lines suggesting bracelets and necklaces and underlining the eyes and covering the eyebrows.

Inscriptions were traced to restore Ramses' identity and to recall the care lavished on his remains by the priests when the looting of the royal tombs was discovered. On the abdomen, in ink, were drawn two large, irregular, cartouches in which one may read in hieroglyphs the coronation name, unusually followed by the name given Pharaoh at birth. Between the cartouches and the knees are lines in hieratic writing mentioning a first text citing the name of the high priest, Herihor (Year 6 under Ramses IX). Almost entirely "erased", this inscription is straddled by a record of Year 10 of the fourth month of the *perit* season on the 17th day. A third record was written at the top of the head, in the same year and the same month, but on the 20th day, thereby sanctioning the end of the operation.

Based on these texts, it is possible to reconstitute the broad outlines of what occurred after the looting of the royal tombs was discovered. The high priest, Heri-hor, ordered the safekeeping of certain mummies, including those of Ramses II and Sethos I. They were brought to the burial vault of Sethos I, seemingly to ensure them of permanent protection. Then, during the reign of Siamun, during the first third of the year 1000 BC, orders were given to protect them from new assaults. The pharaonic bodies gathered in the burial vault of Sethos were secretly transported to the other side of the mountain, south of the site of Deir el-Bahri in the former tomb of Queen Inhapy, near the remains of the deified king Amenophis I, who had already been placed out of harm's way in the heart of the long, rocky area. The transfer—numerous priests and the chief of seals of the necropolis naturally participated—was completed three days later. The text reveals that Ramses' entrance "into the house of eternity of Amenophis" was accompanied by new priests. Ramses was to remain there for 2,900 years without further mishap until looters of the necropolis discovered the "royal *cachette*" between 1871 and 1878.

The lesson of History

Ramses took great care to prepare his immortality. With the passage of time, should one decry the inanity of the rites, the greed or forgetfulness of man and the destructive work of the millennia? Nothing of the kind.

Invasions, earthquakes and sand have failed to completely erase the monumental evidence the great king left behind. And the engraved and sculpted lessons on the walls of these monuments were transmitted from generation to generation. Undoubtedly, the famous Battle of Qadesh, which Ramses had illustrated on at least five walls of his temples, marked for him the decisive turning-point of his reign. His clash with the Hittite armies, bolstered by numerous allied troops, led him to reconsider the orientation of his foreign policy, then, after long preparations, to seal the first international agreement in History. The whole of his reign demonstrates that he conditioned a happy era of peace in the Middle East and this certainly helped mold his legend.

During the period when hieroglyphic writing was indecipherable, the sovereigns of the ancient country of Egypt were designated only by the Hellenized name of "pharaoh". The name of Ramses, however, came down through the centuries and remained alive.

Battle of Qadesh

The most specific retelling of the Battle of Qadesh—the "bulletin"—is in Abydos, in Luxor at the Ramesseum and at Abu Simbel. The drawings exhibited come from the latter temple. The king also organized the glorification of his exploits in the form of a genuine *chanson de geste*—the *Poem of Pentaweret*. Like everything the pharaohs had represented on the walls of their temples, it was clearly based on an historical event. It is reflected in the Hittite archives, composed of tablets engraved in cuneiform signs, discovered at Boghaz Köy in Anatolia.

The Egyptian text of the bulletin, illustrated with extremely vivid reliefs, reveals that the young Ramses crossed the border at the fortress of Tjaru (El Qantarah) in Year 5 of his reign, the second month of the Summer season on the ninth day. He took the coastal road, dotted with wells guarded by Egyptian fortresses, restored by his father, Sethos I. After crossing Canaan, he entered the country of Amurru. He passed by Pi-Ramses-of-the-Valley-of the Cedars—probably the future Byblos—to branch off slightly to the south of Tripoli toward the Orontes River. Probably in Year 4 of his reign, Pharaoh set up a garrison of well-prepared troops, the Nearin.

The road then taken by the king was most likely that which led to the Biqa plain in order that he might arrive from the southwest in the direction of the city of Qadesh. No one knows if Ramses' goal was really to confront the allied forces in this region. Some Hittite documents—"the letter of the general" (Hittite), among others sent by the general to his ally, the king of Ugarit—imply that Ramses, believing his enemies were stationed between the city of Halba and the Eleutherus more to the north, sought to surprise them by a turning movement, passing by the southwest of Qadesh. Unfortunately, spies had falsely informed the king.

Believing he was far from his adversaries and finding his army's progress too slow—his army consisted of four divisions of some 20,000 to 25,000 infantrymen and charioteers—he separated from the main force with only his Amun division and bivouacked on the left bank of the Orontes before Qadesh. Ramses had left Egypt exactly one month before. His soldiers had just captured two alleged stragglers from the enemy army. After a serious beating, they admitted they had been ordered to supply misleading information. In reality, the Hittite army was close by, hidden behind Qadesh on the right bank, and set to attack.

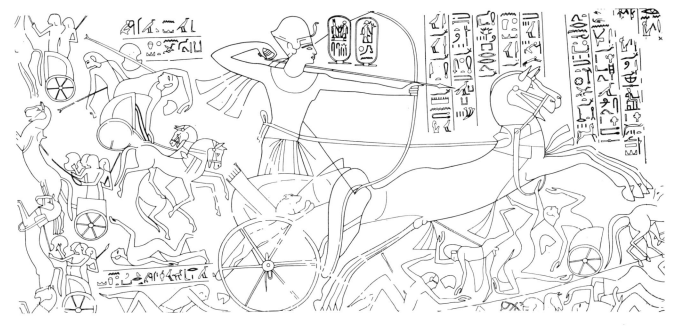

Ramses gathered together his war council, admonished his vizier and officers for their negligence and gave orders that the Re division, which was near the ford of the Shabtuna, a ten-kilometre march from there, be hastily warned. Even farther away, crossing the woods of Robaoui, was the Ptah division. Finally, ten kilometres away, was the Seth (or Sutekh) division.

The royal chariot, fortunately, was hitched up. Soon after, Pharaoh's camp was invaded by the first Hittite attackers. Their army was made up of more elements than Pharaoh's. Surprised as well, the Egyptians, their chariots unharnassed, were helpless, the troops busy grooming the horses, feeding them, repairing weapons, wrestling or even sleeping. Erect on his chariot, Pharaoh charged into the fray with Menna, his shield-bearer, finding himself almost alone to fight 2,500 enemy chariots. Amun heard his call. Ramses burst onto the battlefield like "a flame on straw", giving some of his soldiers time to regroup. The struggle, however, was truly too lopsided. If fresh reinforcements, the Nearin, had not come to the rescue, Ramses would certainly have been killed. Still, he devastated the immediate shore of the Orontes. Countless numbers of adversaries were shot through with arrows or fell into the river.

Then, the enemy prince, standing on his chariot, raised his hand to halt the attack. His troops quickly returned to the Qadesh citadel. Located on the present site of Tell Nebi Mend (Laodicea), not far from the ruins of the "Krak des Chevaliers", it evokes the vestiges of a citadel of the Crusades. Qadesh was not occupied by the Egyptians as the Hittite archives gloriously recall. Ramses was unable to regain the strategic point which locked, so to speak, the Egyptian zone of influence in the Middle East, formerly occupied by the great Tuthmosis III of the 18th dynasty.

The night of the battle, the king counted his losses and those of the enemy, had the spoils gathered together, congratulated himself for having avoided a defeat which had appeared inescapable and left the battleground to change his strategy.

General Cairo catalogue: 616

Dimensions: *Medium*
Height: 0.80 m   Black granite
Width: 0.70 m

Technique
Must have been stuccoed and probably painted, with gilding

Condition   *Provenance*   *Date*
Good   Tanis (Sân el-Hagar)   Ramses II

Bibliography
Encyclopédie photo, Pl. 142, p. 42
Terrace and Fischer, *Treasures of Egyptian Art from the Cairo
   Museum*, London, 1970, pp. 141-144, No. 32

Desroches Noblecourt *et alii*
Catalogue of the Ramsès le Grand exhibition, Paris, 1976, No. XVI, pp.
   84-85

The fragmentary inscription engraved on the back of the statue—"the living god of great victories . . ." is certainly, in itself, insufficient to identify the figure. Nevertheless, Egyptologists do not doubt this black granite bust is a portrait of the great pharaoh. Indeed, there are too many points of resemblance not to accept this interpretation. The round, full wig made of small curls framing the face without uncovering the ears, the motifs on the headband and the shape of the *uraeus*, the plated strip at the top of the forehead under the wig, the wide, slightly arched eyebrows, the shape of the eyes, the fleshy mouth of his daughter, Meryeta-mun (cf. 28) and the small chin of his mother Tuya (cf. 5), all the features of his family are brought together in this figure of the master of Egypt.

Like his daughter, the king wears a wide necklace with four rows of bars ending in a series of drops. However, this jewelry is masculine and does not cover the shoulders like a collar. The pleated robe on one shoulder and, on the edge, wide sleeves, knotted under the right breast, recall the costume of the beginning of the reign, itself influenced by the fashion initiated under Amenophis IV-Akhenaten. The right forearm of the sovereign, folded over the chest, is adorned on the wrist with a bracelet decorated with the *wadjet* eye. The king holds in his hand the *heqa* hook, only traces of which remain. It was one of the emblems of the royalty of Upper Egypt, inherited from the god Osiris. On this statue should be noted an anatomical feature not found on likenesses of his subjects but which clearly appears on the royal images of Amenophis IV—the pectoral nipple protrudes considerably and is visible even under the robe. Another detail should be pointed out: the head of the sovereign gives the impression the bust is slightly leaning forward. Its attitude suggests that of the famous likeness of Ramses in Turin. It certainly helps understanding to realize that royal statues, to date, are all shown distributed symmetrically on each side of a "line of frontality". During the reign of the monarch, there was greater flexibility in an attempt to discreetly introduce the approach of the civilian portrait which was closest to reality. The slightly leaning attitude of the king may also be explained by the observations of numerous physicians who examined Ramses' mummy during its Paris study to save it from the fungus eroding it. Ramses may have suffered from such severe arteriosclerosis that, beginning at about 40 years of age, he perhaps adopted the habit of walking slightly stooped.